It is said that you will meet a few significant people in your lifetime who will touch your soul and help define who you are. I had the extraordinary, unexpected joy of meeting one of those beautiful souls who surely changed my very being and touched my heart deeper than he may ever know. Thank you Matteo, for being God's gift to this world.

He has taught me more about life, happiness, faith and pure love in the few hours that I've been in his presence than I've learned in all of my 46 years of living. Thank you my new friend, for giving me my "Happy Day!"

Jodi Lundell
Attended Matteo's, "Wonders of Autism" presentation
in Lake City, MN

Matteo has helped me affirm a global understanding regarding the amazing potential that lies locked up within these special people. He has given me more insight that confirms what I have always felt. This insight has enhanced the physical therapy, MNRI and Shafaw work I do nationally and internationally. I am able to spread his message to teachers, therapists and parents all over the world. I want to thank Matteo and Annette for letting me be part of Matteo's growth and development.

Diane Whiteside
PT, MNRI Core Specialist
Instructor, Shafaw Method

Matteo is an extraordinary, very talented person. Being Matteo's friend has changed the way I look at things. His story through autism has inspired me in many different ways. I am very fortunate that I have gotten to know him.

Alyson Dillon
Sixth Grade Student

After decades of miraculous healings, I came to know the young Rumi/Matteo Musso. Yet, nothing prepared me for the light of this young man and his ability to touch base with the morphogenetic fields of *knowing* any time he wanted.

Teo brought to my attention that people with autism speak a different language and it is time for me to learn their language before they speak mine. Teo, poetically, is a reminder for us all that we are Spiritual beings having Human experiences and NOT the other way around.

I am looking forward to working with him in *Shafaw Sanctuary of Healing Lights* to bring accelerated healing to autistic children.

Master Healer Behrooz Donadoost
Novato, California

Matteo is an amazing person who has had a huge impact on my life. His journey with autism is an inspiring story that changed how I look at things. He is an imaginative, talented person and I am happy he is my friend.

Haley Moore
Sixth Grade Student

Matteo has always been a part of my life, but until the last two years, just a loveable, happy boy with autism. How that has changed! Those of us who have been fortunate to be a part of his life are not only amazed by his intelligence and perceptiveness, but extremely blessed by his spiritual presence.

Ruth Wedge
Lake City, Minnesota

HANDBOOK OF US

UNDERSTANDING AND ACCEPTING

PEOPLE WITH AUTISM

Matteo Musso

Over The Fence Publishing
Livermore, California

This book is dedicated to all people
who want hope for the future and
who struggle to be heard
in this world.

"If God wanted us to be exactly the same, we wouldn't have had to wait for Dolly, the cloned animal. He'd just crank us out on an assembly line."

Matteo Musso • June 30, 2016

Matteo Musso/Over The Fence Publishing
P.O. Box 2227
Livermore, California 94551
www.matteomusso.com
info@matteomusso.com

Publisher's Note: The intent of this book is to provide ac-curate general information in regard to the subject matter covered. If medical advice or other expert help is needed, the services of an appropriate Medical Professional should be sought. This book is not intended as a substitute for medical advice from a qualified physician. All brand names and product names used in this book or trademarks, regis-tered trademarks, are trade names of their respective holders. Some names have been changed out of respect for privacy.

Please be clear that the author nor the publisher is in any way advising anyone to follow or reject any kind of treatment, medical or otherwise, in this book. Parents and Guardians are urged to obtain as much information as possible when making any decisions that may affect the health and overall well-being of their children, and it is always advisable to consult a health care professional. No warranty, express or implied, is delivered by the author or publisher with respect to the contents of this book.

Book Layout © 2016 BookDesignTemplates.com
Cover Design and Editing by Michelle Hughes

Handbook Of Us/ Matteo Musso. -- 1st ed.
ISBN 978-0-9988636-2-7

Dad, G'pa Frank, G'ma Mary and me, Papa, G'ma Lucia,
Mom and Great Aunt Lillian

ACKNOWLEDGEMENTS

I am grateful to Grandma Mary and Papa for always loving me and to Grandma Lucia, whose life has been full of lessons and learning. You are an inspiration. To Grandpa Frank and Aunt Lillian, who supported our journey, always. To all our family and friends who allowed me to be me, even through my most challenging times. Thanks for sticking with us and not running for the hills! And finally, to Mom and Dad, who never stop looking for ways to make my life wonderful.

I would also like to thank Soma Mukhopadhyay for believing in our intelligence and sharing her gifts of discovery with the world. To Lenae Crandall for patiently helping me find my voice. To Dr. Svetlana Masgutova, Diane Whiteside and the many hands and hearts that have worked toward my development. To Master Behrooz Donadoost for your guidance and healing. And thanks to the many friends and programs which have contributed to my growth and well being.

CONTENTS

Foreword

Prepare yourselves, my friends, to be transformed by Teo's message, awed by his intelligence, humored by his quick wit, and touched by his incredible heart. Teo is a wise and insightful thirteen-year-old autistic boy who has recently found his voice through SOMA Rapid Prompting Method (SOMA RPM). He and his mother, Annette, have had a profound influence on my life, the lives of my family and countless other people fortunate enough to know him and travel this journey of autism with them. I am impressed by the dedication, positive spirit, and humor that has brought Teo to where he is today.

My journey with Annette started at Luther College in Decorah, Iowa, where we shared a passion for piano and became inseparable friends. This friendship continued after graduation when Annette went off to graduate school, and I started my teaching career. Even though we were geographically miles apart, we remained present in each other's lives. We marked milestones together, celebrating our joys and supporting each other as we faced life's challenges.

One of these milestones was the much anticipated birth of Teo. He progressed as a typical infant and toddler, but at 18 months of age, we all noticed a change in his development. I remember the day Annette asked me if I thought Teo was autistic. We had a particularly trying day of shopping with whom we wanted to believe was just an over-stimulated toddler. I did not want to validate her concerns, because as an educator, I knew the challenges facing autistic children and their families. In reality, I recognized the potential signs, but fought to give in to my concerns. Weeks later, Annette called me in tears and shared a diagnosis given to them by their doctor. "Teo is autistic," she said. My heart dropped. After the initial shock, Annette vowed to do everything she could to discover Teo's real gifts. She knew they were there. Annette and Mark have remained true to this vow. What an inspiration!

Our family has always cherished the times when Annette, Mark, and Teo would come to Minnesota and spend time at our home. Our children became more like siblings to Teo, and my husband and I took on the honored role as his uncle and aunt. Before Teo was able to communicate, a typical visit included opening all the cupboards in our kitchen and showing his delight or frustration through loud outbursts while finding comfort through repetitive actions. Teo was consumed by joy when he was loading and unloading the dishwasher. He always left us with very clean dishes! Teo also loved pepperoni and equally enjoyed tossing pepperoni down our stairwell. He enthusiastically devoured as many chocolate chip cookies as he could sneak out of our ever-changing hiding places and faithfully watched the same movies from beginning to end. Through all of this, we accepted him for who he was and loved everything that was Teo - that "knowing" twinkle in his eye, the hovering presence which spoke of the desire for inclusion, and the many glimpses of brilliance that longed to break free from what we now know was his veil of autism. We believed wholeheartedly that there was something special about him and supported Annette and Mark in their quest to unlock this hidden gem.

For almost a decade, Annette and Mark were unstoppable as they navigated different types of autism therapies and collaborated with school educators and other specialists to design an appropriate education for Teo. They worked tirelessly to get assistance for the ever increasing cost of helping their son. Then, one beautiful day in April of 2015, I received another tearful phone call from Annette. This time, tears of joy flowed as she shared Teo's first session using RPM. Teo was able to answer simple questions and spell out words that they didn't realize he even knew. I was blown away by her description of the session and excited as she relived every moment. I did not understand what RPM was or what was happening until I got to see it first hand, the transformation of our Teo. I believe he has just begun to show us the extent of his gifts.

Teo has made a significant impact on my sixth grade students and fellow teachers who have been fortunate to hear his story. Teo and

Annette have given us a personal glimpse into their ongoing joys and struggles as well as their aspirations for the future. During their visits to our school, my students have been enthralled, entertained, inspired, and educated about autism. More importantly, they have formed a personal connection with Teo. Because he shares his life so openly with others, my students have become more accepting of their peers, and they are more willing to embrace and celebrate each person's unique differences. As teachers, we have been given a special look into a child with autism. We are encouraged to "assume intelligence" when we are fortunate to have one of these unique learners in our classroom who teach us so much. Since Teo's communication evolution, we have had aha moments regarding the meaning of autism. We can discover treasures waiting to be found despite the challenging diagnosis; we only need to find the key to open the door to their communication and self-expression. Teo has helped to validate the importance of accepting all students for who they are and to cherish the unique gifts they have to give the world.

Teo was able to use the letter board to communicate his own thoughts and offer support to us from afar as we experienced the difficult times surrounding my dad's death from cancer. We were all surprised at the wisdom and depth of this young boy. His words changed our whole outlook as we dealt with this overwhelming loss. Teo always seemed to know what we needed - a boost of positivity, a poem filled with incredible insight, or a writing which showered us with humor. This is something he was previously unable to do. Now his treasured visits to Minnesota include showing his "knowing" twinkle through poetry, heartfelt thoughts, or the occasional sarcastic jibe. He loves sharing his quest for inclusion and acceptance with audiences of all ages. His waves of brilliance and insight are beautiful.

I am so blessed to call Teo my cherished friend. I know he will continue to inspire the same positive change in our world that he has in mine.

Anne Solberg
Zumbrota, MN
6th Grade Teacher, Zumbrota-Mazeppa Elementary School

Editor's Note

This boy, Matteo Musso, is pure love, joy, forgiveness and complete acceptance. He is only thirteen and yet way beyond most adult's capacity to understand life, love and God.

I was invited to come and meet Matteo, by his mother Annette. They were looking for an editor, book preparer for Matteo's first book. I had no idea what to expect. Annette greeted me at her door with a huge, warm smile as I walked into the Musso home. Matteo was right there, too, greeting me in his way with a direct look like he was "checking me out." Then he comfortably weaved in and out of us while we talked.

As Annette and I sat on the couch, Matteo continued to hover near us during our conversation. I think he was walking around eating a bite of pizza on a plate. He would come over and touch his mom's neck with a gentle, loving touch, look into her eyes, then walk away again. I could see the love he had for his mom. They would frequently hug, laugh and be silly. He seemed to love that.

Matteo's movement and behavior reminded me of what it would be like to follow pure desire with no filter. Like running up and grabbing your girlfriend, jumping up and down, screaming in happiness to see each other. Or walking up to a stranger because you were drawn to their fuzzy sweater that you just had to feel for yourself. There was this feeling of freedom in the Musso home. There was joy in this house, joy and acceptance. I could also see that Matteo had appropriate social skills to be easy going and friendly with company. My gosh, to be at ease and free to take care of yourself in the moment, what has happened to us as a society? There are protocols and formalities that keep a distance between us. All of this love and relaxed atmosphere was rubbing off on me. I found myself over at the busy, joyful Musso house feeling the freedom of relaxed acceptance.

One afternoon, Matteo's Dad, Mark, joined in the conversation and told a story I found hilarious. He and Matteo were shopping at the grocery store and a customer approached Mark and said, "your son just took a bite out of a loaf of bread and put it back!" Mark said, "Okay, thanks." This guy was beside himself. I guess he expected a stern chastising of Matteo. The guy said, "That's it?" Obviously he wasn't aware that Matteo was not your usual person. "There's fresh bread. I'm hungry. I'm taking a bite." Why not?! That's logical, right? Mark calmly said to his son, "Let's go buy some bread Matteo." Of course, he intended to purchase the bread. This casual, comfortable acceptance is so refreshing to me.

For the first time, I began to see something awe-inspiring; that maybe, just maybe, autism is here to wake us up out of a deep sleep and to show us a purity of love that our humanity has lost. Well, this is exactly what I am being shown by Matteo.

One afternoon while picking photos for this book, I looked over at Annette and asked her, "What is the biggest affect Matteo's autism has had on you?" She said without missing a beat, "My priorities have changed drastically. How others judge me and my son has no influence on my emotional state now. My son's comfort and well-being is always my priority, no matter where we are." Annette shared that Matteo had a melt-down in the airport during Christmas a few years ago. He was screaming at the top of his lungs and basically paralyzed in his body from the stress. The jam-packed Christmas airport travellers were all looking. Yet, all she could think about was her son. No one else could see what was going on inside of him, extreme duress and sensory overload. But she knew. To sit there, in whatever public situation, holding him, comforting him, giving him relief for as long as it takes, is her priority. She can now do this, completely oblivious to those around them. "It definitely took a lot of practice!" she chuckled. Annette reminds Matteo that if people knew what was really going on with him, their compassion would come through immediately. They just don't know.

Matteo's best friend is Christ, Jesus. That is a big pill to swallow. I am a spiritual person but not necessarily Christian-based. I believe in Jesus and I do believe very much in the love and friendship that Matteo has with him. What Matteo shares about God and God's love for us is other-worldly, and I would say, even Divine. It is my opinion that Matteo is obviously talking to God, sharing wisdom beyond most human's capacity, offering messages of love and hope that could only come from God, the Source, our Creator, or Christ Jesus.

I saw Matteo speak in front of a large class of college psychology students. He was just himself. Walking and wandering around not nervous at all, he was just a person enjoying himself, touching a desk, eating chocolate cookies (given to him by the receptionist at the department's front desk, as they checked in!) and walking in and out of people.

When it was time, his mom directed him and they went up front. She gave some background information to the group and then put the stencil like letter board in front of Matteo. He immediately focused and began pointing. One by one, individual letters became words, then sentences, then complete thoughts. Unrehearsed, unedited, it flowed. "Hi. Nice to see everyone here. I recognize a few faces." The room went silent. Mouths fell open. I am not exaggerating.

Matteo knew why he was there and he knew what the students were interested in. What Matteo taught was that he was completely present, even though his body did not tell that story, prior to sitting at the letter board. Matteo took command of the room with his words, as he discussed many topics of love, positivity, and what it's like to be autistic.

So here we are. This is Matteo's first book. It is important to know that it was written without corrections. Without jumbled words or letters to be reorganized. No, this book unfolded letter by letter. I am guessing it was pre-organized in his head somewhere. I want you to remember that this author is a young man of only thirteen years. His words must be inspired from elsewhere. What I see is a wise, enlightened soul who is sharing information through a boy named

Matteo, this beautiful and very "present" son of Annette and Mark Musso.

I believe Matteo, and these other "angels" with autism, are a gift to this world. I thank Mark and Annette, for birthing and nurturing this beautiful being. He is teaching something profound and unique to all of us. From what they have told me, Mark and Annette had no idea, that from shock and fear, would come exhilaration and the amazing gifts Matteo is giving. I share in the wonderful joy and celebration that is your son. And thank you, God.

Michelle Hughes
Editor

How This Book Was Written

This first book from my son, has taken 18 months and countless hours for him to author. It was written one letter at a time pointing at a letter board. Due to autism, my son has very limited speech, and yet so much to say.

Matteo can use language to basically get his needs met or express short requests of two to six words, but he's not a verbal conversationalist. He is challenged to express original thoughts, feelings or answer the question, "How was your day?"

So, as you read this book, try to imagine me and my 11 and a half year old son sitting on the couch, day after day, letter by letter, getting to know each other for the first time. We stayed up until midnight many nights "chatting" away. We just couldn't get enough since his entire lifetime together, of conversations and questions, were bottled up inside us.

The only reason we are able to have these gifts of conversation is due to *SOMA RPM*, the *Rapid Prompting Method*. Matteo spells out his thoughts, letter by letter, pointing to an alphabet stencil made out of really high-tech materials...laminated paper or stenciled out of a piece of lucite. I do not touch him at all during this process or facilitate any of his words. RPM is not to be confused with Facilitated Communication.

He never corrects any statements or wants to erase anything, thoughts just flow out perfectly the first time! This is also true in his poetry. It's like it is divinely inspired so it's perfect immediately. No editing, no re-wording, no misspelling of words. His vocabulary is one of the things that shocked us the most! When he's asked why he knows such mature language, he says that he's been read to and he's been listening his entire life. "You can learn a lot when you really listen."

At the beginning of our RPM journey together, Matteo would point to a single letter and I'd write it down. Then he'd point to the next, and I'd write. Hours and hours would pass to get a paragraph of back and forth thoughts out, but what a conversation we'd have! As we got more fluent doing RPM together, the single letters turned into entire words. He'd point M-O-M (I'd write Mom), C-A-N (I'd write "can") W-E (write) G-O (write) T-O (write) D-I-S-N-E-Y (write) L-A-N-D (write). We graduated to entire sentences (MOM, WHERE DID YOU HIDE THE CHOCOLATE?) and that's how this entire book was written!

Matteo shared with us that he wanted to write this book back in August, 2015. That's when his introduction was written. Mark and I hope you enjoy this gift from our son. We wished we'd had this insight given to us by an autistic person right after Matteo was diagnosed. Wow, our early years would have been an entirely different journey than the one we had. Yet, we are grateful for every step of our journey with our son, as the path we walked brought us here. We live such an exciting life with him. Believe me, there's never a dull moment around here! Matteo's insights and inspired thoughts blow us away every day as they challenge our beliefs and open our eyes and hearts to new concepts and possibilities.

Enjoy! *Annette Musso*

RPM Beginnings

My friend and *RPM* teacher, Lenae.

January 2015: Emma Epphard, a *Son-Rise* mom friend of mine in Illinois told me I *had* to check out a new thing she was doing with her son called *Soma RPM, Rapid Prompting Method*. She exclaimed that she is "getting to know her son" for the very first time!

February 2015: I scheduled an in-home Outreach with an *RPM*-trained therapist from Utah, Lenae Crandall. The earliest she could come to our home was May 7-9, 2015. I booked her.

March 2015: I tried to get 1:1 sessions with Lenae when she came to San Jose, but the waiting list was too long. I encouraged her to hold a Q and A session for parents like me who need some questions answered and had great interest in the method. I was teaching myself using the resources available (books, *SOMA RPM* website, Facebook Groups, etc.). She obliged and held the meeting for about 15 of us. All were having success communicating with their children. I WAS HOOKED! Even before this meeting, with TeamTeo torn between the concepts of *Son-Rise* and *RPM*, we felt Matteo was enjoying himself more and loving the academic stimulation. I also tried to enter the lottery for training at the Institute in Austin, Texas, but was unable to succeed online. I will still work on that!

April 2015: I was able to meet a *Son-Rise/RPM* mom in Dublin, Krassi, who has a 9 year old son. She's been doing *RPM* for 2 years and invited me to her home to watch her work with her son. I jumped on that, of course! What I saw was amazing. He comprehended everything she taught him and got 100 per cent of the questions correctly during her "teach-ask" session. I was still trying to secure some sessions with Lenae during her April trip to the Bay Area. It was really tough! I had to be very persistent (sort of an excited and motivated nuisance). My new friend Krassi, graciously gave us 3 of her days. What a gift! I'll never be able to repay her.

April 24, 2015: MY LIFE CHANGED FOREVER! I heard my son's unique, creative thoughts for the first time in his life! Below is a synopsis of what happened. BOLD print indicates Matteo's unprompted words that he spelled out letter by letter.

These are the first few days:

DAY 1 • April 24, 2015 • Session 1 • 30 minutes

Lenae Crandall, our *RPM* teacher, taught Matteo about giant eels today. "They are slimy and wriggle to move through the water. What other animals "wriggle" to move?

Matteo: **SNAIL, SNAKE**

Then Matteo was asked to finish these sentences. (His answers are in caps.)

If I met an eel I would _____. **SCREAM**
Eels are _____. **GROSS**
The coral reef is _____. **FUN**
Why?_____. **I CAN SWIM**

Lenae then asked him to spell three things he thinks of surrounding the word "swim."

FLOAT, MAKE A CASTLE, BIRTHDAY

Lenae asked him to spell 3 things he thinks of surrounding the word "eel."

BLOODY, GROSS, MEAN

After the eel lays her eggs, she dies.
Complete this sentence,

Death of an eel is _____. COOL
When an eel dies it is _____. BLOODY
Blood is _____. RED
Red is _____. GROSS
Mom is _____. MY MOST FAVORITE.
Why?_____ SHE CARES ABOUT ME. MOM IS
MY GREAT FRIEND.

Lenae explained that Mother's Day is coming up
and asked Teo to tell her something about
mothers.

Moms are _____. GREAT COOKS

DAY 2 • April 25, 2015 • Session 1 • 30 minutes

On the way to our session with Lenae, I asked
Teo if he would mind if I asked him some
questions during the session today and he could
choose to answer them or not. He said, "Yes."

Mom: "Why do you cover your ears?

Matteo: I JUST DO SO MY HEAD DOESN'T
SPIN.
(Mom is crying at this point. Matteo continues)

XX

Matteo: I AM ALWAYS SPINNING. I CAN'T STOP. HOW IS *NOT* SPINNING?

Lenae: Is that a question for your mom to answer?

Matteo: YES. (I didn't have an answer for him)

Lenae: Are you dizzy when you spin?"

Matteo: NO, IT IS MY REALITY.

Lenae: How does covering your ears help?"

Matteo: IT CALMS ME DOWN.

Lenae: This is good information because if people see you covering your ears they might think you don't like sound. Does sound bother you?

Matteo: NO

Lenae: Why are you covering your ears more lately? Are you spinning more now?

Matteo: YES.

Lenae: Do you know why?

Matteo: NO. I CHANGE INSIDE THOUGH, I FEEL.

Mom: Is there anything I can do to help?

Matteo: THANKS FOR ASKING.
(Mom is crying now.)

Matteo: NO GOOD CRYING. I AM FINE.

Mom: I can't help it. I'm so happy that's all
I can do!

Matteo: SO I'M PLEASING YOU THEN?

Mom: Yes Sweetie! You please me every minute!

Lenae: What's your favorite subject to learn
about?

Matteo: I DON'T KNOW YET. I NEED AN
EDUCATION.

> *Matteo said out loud, "DOCTOR"* then
> continued spelling the following...

Matteo: I DON'T WANT TO SHARE MY
THOUGHTS

> *Again he verbally said, "Dr. Stalker",* then
> continued spelling...

Matteo: ON SCHOOL IN MY CURRENT STATE.

XXII

Matteo verbally said, "Mom...Dr. Stalker".
Mom asked him if he wanted to see Dr.
Stalker after this session. He said "yes"
but spelled...

Matteo: NO. I JUST CAN'T STOP SAYING
HIS NAME.

Mom: So that's why you say the same words
over and over?

Matteo: YES. I DON'T NEED AN ANSWER.
JUST MAKE ME STOP.

Mom: How? What would make you stop? Teo
picked his nose and Mom said, "I'd like to make
you stop that!")

Matteo: NOTHING. I DON'T KNOW.
He picked his nose again. Lenae gives him a
Kleenex.

Lenae: Use this so you won't get embarrassed.
(We all chuckled.)

Mom: I don't think he gets embarrassed.

Matteo: I DO...YOU CAN'T IMAGINE IT.
Mom: What do you think about all the current
therapies and activities we are doing?

Matteo: I AM INTO *RPM*. I HATE THE
ANXIETY OF THE ONE CALLED SPEECH.
IT DRIVES ME CRAZY.

Lenae: Why?

Matteo: TOO MUCH PRESSURE.

Mom: How do you feel when you are at church?

Matteo: CHURCH IS GOOD. I LIKE YOUR
LESSONS.

DAY 2 • April 26, 2015 • Session 2 • 30 minutes

Matteo: I NEED MY HEAD DOWN NOW.

Lenae: You have 23 minutes. (Teo's head was
resting on the table.) Are you spinning a lot?

Matteo: NO. I AM INTO SLEEP.

Mom: Tell us more about church. (I wanted to
know if it's too loud or crowded for him.)

Matteo: I AM HAPPY THERE.

Lenae: Is there anything you want Mom and Dad
to know? Or anyone else?

Matteo: TONS. I HAVE NO PATIENCE WITH
SONRISE BECAUSE I AM AWARE OF SKILLS.
I NEED *RPM* ONLY. I KNOW MY SOCIAL
SKILLS GIVE THE IMPRESSION I DON'T,

XXIV

BUT I GET IT.

(*Son-Rise* is wonderful but does not teach any academics. Obviously, Teo was ready for some and needed challenging stimulation!)

Mom: Why do you need the tv turned off immediately after a movie ends?

Matteo: I HAVE NO MORE TO WATCH SO I NEED IT OFF. IT IS OCD (Obsessive Compulsive Disorder).

Mom: Why do you stare at the wall or ceiling sometimes?

Matteo: MY MOM, I AM AUTISTIC.

Mom: What does that mean to you?

Matteo: SO I AM STUCK OFTEN. AUTISM IS NOT MY FAVORITE THING BUT I CAN SAY I'VE GOT SKILLS. I AM INTELLIGENT.

Mom: Do you want me to continue to help you talk?

Matteo: NOT NOW. *RPM* PLEASE. STILL I CAN'T TALK. IT IS ALL JUST WORDS, NOT MEANING.

DAY 3 • April 27, 2015 • Session 1 • 30 minutes

Today is poetry day. Lenae taught Matteo about

"Terse Verse." It's a style of poetry that has a long title and a short verse consisting of 2 words that rhyme. For example: What does a fox call rabbits? A *beast feast*! She explained about rhyming words and that sometimes they may sound the same at the end of the word, but they are spelled differently like high/die. For example: What do you call a kennel when the sprinkler turns on? A *soggy doggy*.

Lenae: Teo, give me some words that rhyme with each other.

Matteo: HIDE/SIDE, RITE/FIGHT, MOM/BOMB

Lenae: Can you make a Terse-Verse using mom/bomb?

Matteo: WHAT DO YOU CALL A FAST LADY? A mom bomb!

Lenae: Awesome! Give me two more rhyming words.

Matteo: EATING/MEETING

Lenae: Oh, ok. Make one using those words!

Matteo: WHAT DO YOU CALL A MIGHTY SHARING OF FOOD? An eating meeting!

Lenae: Wow! You're really good at these! How about another one?

Matteo: WHAT DO YOU CALL A FISH IN A

DISH? Hiding siding.

Lenae: I think you really need to submit these to Laffy Taffy so they can print them on the back of their wrappers. What do you think about when I say Laffy Taffy?

Matteo: SWEET, MINI, CHRISTMAS

Then Lenae told The Ant and the Grasshopper fable.

Lenae: What was the ant doing?

Matteo: WORKING

Lenae: What about the grasshopper?

Matteo: DANCING AND SINGING

Lenae: What do you think the moral of this fable is?

Matteo: DON'T PROCRASTINATE

Day 3 • April 27, 2015 • Session 2 • 30 minutes

This time it was my turn to teach Matteo the lesson and get feedback from Lenae. I thought it went quite well but have a long way to go. Teo would answer my questions and was not using language (a good thing as it's getting in the way right now).

After my feedback from Lenae, I asked him how he heard about OCD (he mentioned that he has it the other day).

Matteo: I HEAR IT OFTEN. I GET STUCK IN RITUAL.

Lenae: Any feedback for your mom?

Matteo: NOW I THINK SHE DID WELL, BUT NO CHEERING.

(In *RPM* we are supposed to keep our voice matched to his excitement level. We don't "blow it up big" as we did in *Son-Rise*.)

Matteo: I AM CONFIDENT SHE WILL DO WELL.

Lenae: Kim's going to do well, too, don't you think?

Matteo: YES. GO KIM GO. (Kim often says, "Go Teo, Go!" It's their "thing." Now he just said it to her!)

Then they did more "teach-ask."

Mom: Which board to you like better, stencil or letter board? (he verbalized letter, but spelled stencil).

Matteo: STENCIL

Lenae: Why?

Matteo: IT IS SOLID AND I POKE IT.

He had one minute left in the session and Lenae started the sentence...

Lenae: Dear World, _____

Matteo: I AM SMART. NO MORE BABY TALK. NO MORE SONRISE. HAVE FUN! LOVE, MATTEO

Lenae thinks Teo would get along very well with another boy so we will do a joint session on Wednesday for a social time! I am so excited! Every day is filled with surprises and miracles!

DAY 4 • April 29, 2015 • Session 1 • 30 minutes

Another miracle! This morning, we were invited to have an *RPM* session with another boy named Evan (he will be 10 years old soon). They each took turns using the letter board which was held by Lenae, the *RPM* "therapist-magnificent"! No words were spoken out loud, only spelled out by pointing to the letter board. Lenae was their scribe.

Before we arrived, Evan had a private session with Lenae and spelled out, "I think Matteo is awesome!"

The boys met after Evan's session. We all re-introduced ourselves to each other and off to the room we went. Mind you, Krassi (Evan's mom) is a *Son-Rise* mom and was generous enough to let me come to their home and observe her doing an *RPM* lesson with Evan so I could learn faster.

Then, since Lenae was full for this trip, Krassi gave us 3 of her days! That is the only way we were to get "in" to see Lenae. Again, she is my HERO and I will forever be thankful to her!

The boys sat side by side at the table and it began...(Matteo had a rainbow colored texturized rubber ball on his lap)

Evan: Hi Matteo.

Matteo: HI EVAN

Evan: How are you?

Matteo: FINE THANKS.
AND YOU?

Evan: Like great! I like your cool ball. (Then Evan reached for the beloved "Rainbow Ball" and Teo turned his back to protect his ball. "Uh-oh," I thought. Then, Evan just scratched it over and over with his fingernails.)
XXX

Matteo: THANKS. NOW MY MOM'S NOT CRAZY, BUT HOW SHE GETS UPSET WHEN I DON'T SHARE! SO, PLEASE CONTINUE TO SCRATCH IT.

Evan: Thanks...can't help myself!

Matteo: I KNOW THE LIKELIHOOD OF IT STOPPING IS NOT GREAT.

Evan: I agree. I am now coloring to stop myself. (Evan started to get frustrated and make high-pitched sounds. Matteo covered his ears.)

Matteo: DO YOU STIM OFTEN?

Evan: No. I do it always. (Now he's standing up, wanting to walk around, etc...Lenae gets him to sit back down. Matteo is still covering his ears and raising his shoulders up.)

Matteo: ME TOO. I HATE NOISE, SO I PLUGGED MY EARS.

Evan: I am sorry. I am feeling hot. (His vocalizations escalate.)

Matteo: (covering his ears with his shoulder and hand) HOW ABOUT YOU MAKE IT SOFTER.

Evan: Sorry. I am so mad I cry.

Matteo: I AM HAPPY YOU ARE MY FRIEND.

Evan: Thanks. Me too.

Matteo: SO, I AM NOW INTO SCIENCE.

Evan: So am I, too.

Matteo: DO YOU LIKE PLANTS?

Evan: Yes. Someday I want some money to make a garden.

Matteo: MAYBE I HAVE AN IDEA. LET'S DO IT TOGETHER!

Evan: Deal!

(The timer goes off and our time is up. Lenae says, "Closing remarks, guys.")

Matteo: TALK LATER.

Evan: Deal! Bye.

When we got in the hallway, I kid you not, Matteo was skipping/prancing down the hallway like a colt set free to run for the first time! It was as if he was going to fly, I'm not kidding! He was smiling, laughing, the happiest I've ever seen him! Then he turned around and ran back to me and gave me the biggest hug in the world! If you could have been in that room, seen and felt the respect and understanding these two young guys were giving each other, I believe you would agree with me that it was the most beautiful scene one could witness. It was a lesson in how we should all be treating each other! MIRACLE MIRACLE MIRACLE!

Stay tuned, we got invited back tomorrow as Lenae is doing sessions in front of some college students. Matteo and Evan will have another session together with the students observing.

Thanks for reading this!!! I want to shout it from the mountaintop, WITH A HUGE MEGAPHONE!!!!!

DAY 4 • April 29, 2015 • Session 2 • 30 minutes

Teo was given a choice of learning about History or Poetry. He chose History. Ancient Greece it is! Since I hadn't taught Teo about our world geography before, Lenae did a quick intro to it.

Lenae: Our world is made up of 7 continents and 4 oceans. She named the 7 continents then asked Teo to name them all. He spelled all 7 of them! Same with the oceans!

She then started to teach about ancient Greece.

Lenae: Teo, what do you think of when you hear the word Ancient?

Matteo: OLD, GRANDMA, DINOSAUR.

Lenae: Give me a sentence using the words

Grandma and ancient.

Matteo: GRANDMA MIGHT BE ANCIENT, BUT HAPPILY ALIVE.

Lenae: Give me a sentence using the word dinosaur.

Matteo: THE DINOSAUR ROAMED THE EARTH.

Onward with the "teach-ask" technique...

Lenae: A peninsula is surrounded on 3 sides by water. What's on its 4th side?

Matteo: LAND.

She talked about the first civilization. It was the Phoenicians. A few minutes later she asked:

Lenae: Who are we talking about?

Matteo: PHOENICIANS (spelled perfectly!)

Lenae: They were Maritime people who relied on water for a living. They worked by or on a river. What do you think about when you hear the word river?

Matteo: WATER, ROARING.

Lenae: What about when you hear mountain?

Matteo: ROCKS, GARDEN.

Lenae: What triggered the word garden? It's kind

of neat but it doesn't connect.

Matteo: MY GARDENS ARE LIKE MOUNTAINS.

Lenae: Is this for real or symbolic? (she asked

me. I said "symbolic, I think...") Matteo, tell me more about that.

Matteo: MY LIFE IS BEAUTIFUL IN THE UP CLIMB.

He learned about the Minoans (spelled it correctly) and remembered Ancient Greece was destroyed by a volcano.

DAY 5 • April 30, 2015 • Session 1 with Evan

The speech pathology professor, Dr. Jean Novak, from San Jose State University was in attendance today with about eight of her students. Most were watching from another room via a live feed from Lenae's camera.

Two of them were in the room with us, as well as Dr. Novak, five of us from the two families, the two boys and Lenae. It was a party!!! It begins...

Matteo: MY LIFE IS GARDENING. HI EVAN.

Evan: Hi Matteo. How are you?

Matteo: GOOD THANKS. AND YOU?

Evan: Happy to be here! Dr. Novak, welcome back.

Dr. Novak: Thank you. It's nice to see you, too.

Evan: How are you?

(Evan just lost his Grandpa in January and helped care for him at their house.)

Dr. Novak: I'm very good. Are you feeling better than last time we were together?

Evan: Yes. My heart is healing.

Dr. Novak: I know. It will take time. I am so glad to see you again and to meet your friend, Matteo.

Matteo: THANKS DR. NOVAK.

Dr. Novak: You're welcome, Matteo. It's nice to see you and have this conversation. I hear that you like gardening.

Matteo: I DO. I WANT TO HAVE A GARDEN WITH EVAN.

Dr. Novak: Oh, that's nice. Do you want your garden to have vegetables or flowers?

Matteo: I THINK BOTH

Dr. Novak: Evan, do you want to have a garden too?

Evan: I do. I want to plant my garden with Matteo.

Dr. Novak: I'm sure when you're all done, you'll invite me over for some flowers and food. I'm sure it will be organic!

Evan: Deal!

Matteo: SO EVAN, HOW IS YOUR LIFE IN GARDENING COMING?

Evan: Like great!

Matteo: THAT IS NICE. WHAT ARE YOUR IDEAS?

Evan: I want to have a party garden with leaves and trees.

Matteo: WELL, I LIKE THAT IDEA. I MIGHT SAY WE MIGHT HAVE FLOWERS AND VEGGIES, TOO.

Evan: I wouldn't want our garden any other way that what you say.

Matteo: I THANK YOU. GOOD MOM, I NEED TO MOVE NEXT TO THE HOUSE BY EVAN.

Lenae: Okay you guys, there are 5 minutes left. Do you want to answer questions from the students here or just let them know your thoughts about autism?

Matteo: ANSWER QUESTIONS.

Evan: Questions, too.

(The students didn't have any...they were in shock, I think)

Lenae: Okay then. Matteo, what do you think is important for them to know about autism?

Matteo: I SAY I NEED *RPM* SO MUCH. NEED TO COMMUNICATE SO BAD! THIS EVAN IS MY ONLY FRIEND SO *RPM* SAVED ME. (You can guess what Mom did at this point, tears.)

Evan: I agree completely. I have few friends, too

Introduction

Q: What would you like people to know about you?

"That I am happy. That I am smart. That I am God's
little messenger and that I love Him."

Q: *If you could give a gift to the world, what would it be?*

"Love without expectations."

I am Matteo Musso and I am autistic. Autism is not a neurological condition but rather a spiritual energy. This is important to know because it affects everything, how you see your child or relative on the spectrum, your students, your patients and yes, your patience! I've wanted to write this book for so long and for so many reasons. First and foremost, God and Mom have given me my voice, so I should really use it. It's not nice to keep gifts in their packages. Secondly, I've been silent for 11 and a half years, so I've got a lot to say. Finally, someone needs to change society's views about autistics...

"He's not present."

"He's not paying attention."

"He doesn't know how to do that."

"He's mentally slow."

"We'd like to add diagnosis of intellectual delay."

"Better do it ten more times to be sure he gets it."

"He likes to be alone. He's not trying."

"He doesn't care about having friends."

"He talks only to get his needs met."

"He doesn't like to be touched."

"Freedom will never be ours because of him."

(Lucky for me, my parents never said that.)

"Stop saying that over and over."

We definitely give you reasons to believe these things but only because you are seeing us from your own life experience. It is my hope that you can see people with autism through the new lens of God.

Listen to our pleas to communicate. We do it so much through non-verbal ways. Love us unconditionally during our meltdowns because that's when we need your love, patience, and acceptance the most. Open your minds to a new way of existence, as we are all different from one another in so many ways.

I invite you to consider changing your attitude about friendship, to start caring about whom you spend your time with. Many spend time with people who do not lift them up. God wants us to have positive thoughts and spread love and hope. That's what I'd like to accomplish with this book. Thanks for reading it.

Happily Yours,
Matteo

CHAPTER ONE

How I Got Here

A bit about how I became autistic is in order, so you can understand not only me but *some* other autistics, too. I remember Christ being a real leader of his chosen people. There are many different types of people on this Earth that need leaders because they have commonalities with each other. When I was about one year old, God and I had a talk. *"Can you be a strong voice for my special group of people?"* he asked me. I was flattered he asked me that. You might think to yourself, "How can he remember something from when he was only one year old?" Well, we all could, but that's an entirely different book! God and I made a pact, and here I am. Questions should have been asked, I suppose, prior to making such a commitment which would affect the lives of so many people I loved, but I just knew God would guide and care for them.

Mind you, don't think I'm speaking for all autistics here, because I'm not sure all were given a choice, but this kid was and I accepted the challenge, quite blind to the details. Hmmm, if I knew then what I know now, would I make the same choice? Yes, I would.

I came into this world with the name my parents chose for me, Matteo. It's Italian for Matthew, which means "gift from God." I feel so blessed to be thought of in that way. Mom tells me that she and Dad tried for three years to make me and finally I arrived. Out of that, they named me Matteo. Talk about how to welcome a guy into this world! I felt so loved and safe and happy. Then, one night when I was fifteen months old, I was sleeping and God came and asked me that big question:

"Hey Teo, would you like to help me with a special task? Your life will have a specific and defined purpose. You'll teach others about the things that really matter so they can learn their lessons deeper and stronger. That's why you all walk the Earth. Learn, learn, and grow. And, you'll have the added benefit of helping others who will need your voice. You will lead an extremely reward-ing life with beautiful hearts surrounding you."
How was that for a sales pitch?

I didn't ask any questions about how this would work, or what this "task" actually was. I just knew God would only love me, so I just trusted and agreed.

God quickly began this process of changing

me from a typical kid into someone quite atypical. It was very scary for me because everything started spinning at unexpected times. We would be in a store, in my bed, or on my bedroom floor.

There was really no rhyme or reason to when it happened. I'd just want it to stop. No one could understand my screams or know how to help me. Mom would hold me tight but she was crying tears of pain, too. Dad was going crazy not being able to fix it. Basically, there were many times throughout the years when all three of us were a mess. But at least we were a mess who loved each other!

CHAPTER TWO

What It Was Like

Poor Mom and Dad, they called and called me. Not on their cell phones but merely across the room. Alas, I did not respond anymore. I had found an ability to escape this new world that was spinning but it came with a price. It was an all-or-nothing type of thing. I could hear mumbled sounds emitting from mouths but couldn't give credence to them while on this vicious spin cycle. Now, however, *Masgutova* work (see resources section) helps so much with that. Mom asked if it's a round and round spinning that makes me dizzy. No, not like the fan spinning round and round. My head kind of leaves my body. It's more like a floating than a spinning. It's floating in the air while I look at everybody. That's why energy work helps so much. I needed help to feel grounded. Mom's touch stops the spinning, too.

I had to start taking control. Stacking blocks and knocking them over became comforting to me. I was the gatherer of materials, the work crew, skilled laborer and even better the general contractor. I was the only one in the world, allowed to bring in the demolition crew. Guess who that was? Me and me alone.

If anyone else dared to destroy my magnificent creation without asking or warning me, a price would have to be paid by them and anyone else within earshot of my super high decibel banshee-like screaming. "How could you, you destroyer of all that is good and safe in this world."

Surely you must know the importance of my tower creation. My only way of passing time in peace while the rest of my world spins out of control. Only I can destroy the safe house and only I will know when that time has come. Surely the time would come to put the so-called blocks away. They were my comfort, my reliable game of control and you wanted them put back on a shelf after only two short hours of playing my comfort game? Others told Mom and Dad not to let me do repetitive stuff for long, that it wasn't good for me. But little did those advisors know about what could have been learned had I been given the choice when to return the blocks to the shelf. My funny Uncle Greggie called my creation, "the great wall of Matteo." I found humor and delight in that name.

Uncle Greggie would visit us when he'd be out here in California on a business trip. He knew and respected the power of the "general contractor." But what he did not realize is that I doubled as a "valet parker of precise alignment and ritual." I was typical among autistics in that I had a deep, fond passion for vehicles. I did not discriminate between them. Two wheels, three, four, six, eight, ten, or eighteen; it didn't matter to me. In fact, all modes of transportation were welcomed into my miraculous modes of transportation fleet. Now, of course, they also had to obey me as I maintained my "General Contractor" status in all aspects of life. But now I was dually General Contractor and Valet Parker extraordinaire.

You've all probably had your car valet parked at some point. They carefully, at least as far as you can see, drive your car to a special designated spot and park it very close to another car. The owner, like you, had given the keys to their $30,000 vehicle to a perfect stranger. And there it sat, patiently waiting for the valet to return at the precise time you wanted it, not a moment before. Would you like it if you returned for your car and it was gone? Admit it, you'd freak out!

Well, Uncle Greggie innocently picked up one of my matchbox cars that had been parked so perfectly between the red race car and yellow truck; precisely where it belonged. Anyone could see how the righteous valet, me, had so eloquently landscaped the family room carpet with a rainbow of cars. Poor Uncle Greggie had obviously had a hard and exhaustive day at work, not able to see into the future to predict the tsunami of tears and screams that would ensue if he were to remove that orange car from its perfectly placed parking space by the fireplace hearth. Before anyone could warn him or stop his wayward behavior, it had happened. He touched it. Not only did he touch it, he actually picked it up. His thumb and other two fingers acting like a giant crane lifting this priceless sculpture, without any warning given! Any general contractor would need to be given proper warning when a huge crane is to be used on a job site!

"Banshee boy" made his grand entrance right then and there. I loudly declared my shock and disappointment at my uncle's behavior. Mom and Dad needed to post a sign on the front door stating, "No Large Cranes Allowed." Ahh, had they only thought of that back then or even realized they wore their own cranes, the Banshee would have reared his head much less often. Anyway, back to my shocked and temporarily paralyzed Uncle. Uncle Greggie is a quick

12

learner and realized the sin of his ways. I'm pretty sure it only took him about 24 short hours to recover.

I would suggest signage be placed on the door if you have a cute banshee in your house, "No Large Cranes Allowed." And when the time comes for beloved cars to be stored for the evening, please give your valet warning and proper lead time to fetch the right cars in the proper order. Is it too much to ask of you? No, but it means the world to us.

CHAPTER THREE

Where Are The Brakes?

Brakes are needed to stop things. "Where do you order them?" wonder all the autistics in this world. "I'll take a few pair." Although, if brakes do their job by their very definition, one should be able to get by with a single set. "What is there to stop?" you ask. Well, the feeling of not being connected to my body, for one. I also experienced abdominal pain, a "bolting" out the door problem I couldn't control, a sensitivity to loud sounds, and an inability to process the complex frequencies from music. On top of all that, most people lacked the ability to understand my needs and challenges. Additionally, I lacked "primitive reflex integration" which meant I couldn't catch myself if I tripped, write very well or relax. I have this feeling of floating, like my head is up high looking down at my body. Herein lies the biggest challenge of autism. We need to feel grounded. Mom found some really extraordinary people to help me become grounded.

So, is one set of brakes enough? Depends on the manufacturer, I suppose. God has a strong reputation, never had a recall. You have the option to choose whatever manufacturer you'd like. I just speak from experience.

Brakes come in many shapes, sizes and forms. Some therapies make really effective brakes. The Mercedes of brakes is the *Masgutova Method* (see resources section). You can read about it. Learn to accept us the way we are today and that's "Autism 101." Then we can build on your learning. *Brain Gym* is awesome and pertinent.

But I must tell you that the Rolls Royce of brakes is something you may be unfamiliar with and will require an open mind to believe and accept. That's, (sit down), energy work: *Shafaw, Cranial Sacral, Reiki* and massage. My parents found this amazing healer for me in their friend and massage therapist, Debra. She combines all of these into an amazing energy dance. I highly suggest you look for special people who do these kinds of things. My *Shafaw* master healer, Behrooz Donadoost, is so full of light and love that it actually tickles sometimes when he works on me. Love energy is a huge set of brakes for us. So make room for love's healing light. It's easier for light to shine when the clouds are gone.

CHAPTER FOUR

We're Not Scary
Just Different

I have noticed that most humans judge each other and themselves way too much. Also autistics are an easy target because some of our challenges and outward displays make people uncomfortable.

I know our bodies can surprise the unsuspecting passerby when our actions are sudden and unsuspecting sounds are emitted from our vocal chords. I can see the fear that some people go through because they do not understand. I know that down deep most want to have compassion for us but fear can quickly take over.

Here's one scenario you may have experienced. Let's take a trip to the grocery store together. Let's imagine you are in the produce section and a grapefruit comes flying your way. It hits you in the arm but it is just a grapefruit, so there are no broken limbs involved. Your head turns in the direction from which the flying grapefruit originated. You see a typical looking kid who is wearing a prideful smile and his horrified mother who is not chastising him in any way. Now what would you do? A.) Yell at the mom and tell her to get her obnoxious kid under control? B.) Cast a disapproving look at the child and the mom? Or C.) Will you think to yourself, "Hmmm, I wonder what's going on. I'll smile with a look of compassion, just in case it's needed." When you choose "C", you help a stressed out autism mom get through a torturous, agonizing trip to the store. Just by smiling and wondering, instead of judging as an initial reaction, you are elevated to "angel of the day" in their eyes. After all, the "grapefruit versus gravity" experiment was performed in the name of science!

It's not just the produce section, either. Another popular spot is the check out line. That was my favorite because of all the candy they keep there. I was on a gluten-free, casein-free, nut-free, sugar-free, low-oxalate diet. I used to scream so loudly in that line, dying for that candy! Mom said she stopped taking me to the store for two solid years. I just couldn't handle the lack of control when I couldn't have the things I wanted. It triggers my OCD (Obsessive Compulsive Disorder). Once I decide something,

I can get caught in a loop in my mind. Deep breathing really helps.

I'd get stuck in this vicious loop and not know how to get out. This just happened to me last night when my new friend was over. He is a "neuro-typical" or what society calls "typical." Anyway, we were on my trampoline playing a game Mom thought of to keep us occupied. She got out the whiffle balls and any other type of balls we had, then put pots throughout our yard. She challenged us to shoot the balls into the pots while jumping on the trampoline. It was fun until I got a ball in the eye. My Papa would call it an "eyeball," I think. He likes puns. No one saw it get me in the eye, but it triggered something in me. A slow, shocked whimper exploded into a full-blown meltdown! I don't have them often anymore so it caught me off guard, too. I needed help.

The worst-case scenario here would have been everyone telling me to be quiet. If I could, I would! Mom helped me by remaining calm, as did my friend's mom. I must admit that my friend didn't quite know what to do. Why would he, after all? Even if he knew I got hit, which he didn't, he wouldn't know what to do. His eyes were wide and he didn't say anything for a while. As I got it together enough to get off the trampoline (it's like I temporarily get paralyzed during these episodes), he said the perfect thing I needed to hear from him, "It's okay, Teo. I understand and am still your friend." I could only respond with one word on my letter board, "Really?" Now that's a true friend.

In general, people want to know how to interact with me. I hear things like, "I'd love to engage with you at coffee time after church. How can I do that in a way that's most comfortable for you?" Here is what I recommend: Approach me softly and put a gentle hand on my shoulder to get my attention. Then say what is on your heart without an expectation of a verbal response or eye contact. If I feel pressured to respond and live up to a societal expectation it can stress me out. If I am capable of a response and feel welcomed at the time, you will get one straight from my heart. Please don't take offense if we do not respond. There could be a zillion things distracting us, depending on the setting where our exchange takes place.

During social time after church, your competition is chocolate muffins layered with multiple conversations. There is lots of visual stimulation. Plus, we had just spent an hour sitting in one really comfortable spot, then moved to a room that echoes and everyone is moving around. It's funny how the different heights of people make a difference to our visual processing. These are all things that can prevent me from being able to respond to you. It's not that we don't love you or appreciate your effort to include us. It's just that we have many obstacles to overcome which you do not have, and you can't necessarily see or imagine them.

You know, accepting us and absorbing us into society, with our surprises, isn't a big mystery. Just treat us as you'd like to be treated if you were in our situation. The "Golden Rule" still applies to all people.

So, the key to being comfortable around an autistic person is to know that under each veil of autism there exists an intelligent being with the same emotions you have.

CHAPTER FIVE

Rollercoaster Emotions

Mom just asked me if I wanted to add anything else to this chapter about my regression into autism. Yes. There are two forms of autism. One is called regressive which is the one I have. That means I was developing "normally" up until the age of seventeen months. There is another type of autism, the one that is developed before you were born. But what happened with me was that I lost the speech I had learned up to that point, about one hundred and fifty words and I was left with seven; Mom, Dad, ball, bye, no, apple, hi. Also, I lost my ability to look at people. I couldn't respond to my name. Sounds became hard to tolerate and everything started spinning. Doing things over and over became comforting to me.

I would rename regression and call it transformation, because this is where my spiritual journey went to a different level. It's important to notice the words that you choose. Regression denotes going backwards. I now see it very differently as a part of an evolution of becoming a special person capable of changing the world by teaching about love, patience, priorities and much more.

You see, we are actually further evolved than most people on this planet. Sure, we have big lessons to learn, but while we learn ours, we can be teaching you yours. Ours may be about patience, acceptance, frustration, creativity in coping, self-judgment and self-esteem. Yours might be about some of the same things but with added complexities thrown in like money, careers, other relationships and other kids.

Okay, lecture over. Now, back to the concept of the emotional rollercoaster ride. As autistics are transforming, you may notice little changes in us over a designated amount of time. Some transformations are fast and others are slow. But they all happen according to God's plan.

Why fast? Well, it's a way of getting the transformation over with quickly and getting on to the adjustment phase. Slower transformations may even go undiagnosed. This poses a different set of challenges and lessons for everyone involved. I don't know which I'd prefer if given a choice, but that's not my department anyway, I just report the news. I'm the Ted Copple of autism. I often feel more like the David Letterman of autism, though. Moody me, I guess.

Then there are those who transformed inside their moms, where it is safe, quiet, warm and there are steady, reliable sounds. Smart! That may be a better option and less shocking for everyone. Really, it's out of our control and in God's hands. He chooses the best approach according to lessons we are here to learn and our exciting, new journey.

So, when you discover you are blessed to hang out with, teach, befriend or raise one of God's messengers, fasten your seatbelts! The ride will be filled with ups and downs and crazy twists and turns. Some of you will be fortunate enough to have those upside-down, loop-de-loop experiences!

Which do you want to have? Think about it, when you go to Disneyland, which do you enjoy more? It's a Small World, where you hear the same thing over and over in different languages and you're with a bunch of babies? Or would you prefer Space Mountain, with its thrilling velocity and twists and turns in the dark? You're strapped in securely and you have no choice but to trust that the head of maintenance has assured the safety of the ride, no matter how exciting it feels inside one's body and heart. The darkness of Space Mountain promises a thrilling ride, as you never know when the next twist or turn is coming, which direction it's going or if it's going down or uphill.

The cool thing about your journey with autism, no matter the capacity with which you are involved, is that you get to choose your ride and your experience! I suppose if you are young in your journey or are just being awakened to it, It's a Small World may be enough to handle. I caution you, however, that song gets stuck in your head. You may acquire numbness to its tune but it lurks in the back of your consciousness, blocking the portals where new tunes are waiting to enter. The driving, pounding rhythm of the Space Mountain theme, however, cannot be memorized, as there are no words to be sung. There's just an inner force that's created, driving you onward.

CHAPTER SIX

Eye To Eye

Eye contact. Now here's a hot topic and big generalization about autism. People make assumptions that it's a skill when, in fact, there are a variety of reasons we may not choose to look at someone.

In your life, have you ever been forced to look someone in the eye? Unfortunately, it's often used as an intimidation technique, don't you think? "Alright little Johnny, look me in the eye and tell me it wasn't you who took your sister's chocolate bar," the mom says from her adult-sized perch. Johnny doesn't welcome meeting his mom's gaze, whether he's innocent or not! ECIT! Eye Contact Intimidation Technique. Do they teach it to parents before they have a baby? This can be scary for any child. Or maybe there is a class anyone can take on it because other people use it, too. Let's see, I've observed it in schools, churches, libraries, social gatherings, and yes, every autism therapist on the planet.

Eye contact isn't always what it's cracked up to be.

Stare into someone's eyes for a solid fifteen seconds and then tell me how you feel. Seriously. Notice every sensation in your body. If you really want a challenge, try thirty seconds! Autism heightens our sensory experience by five, ten, or one hundred times, so you may get an idea what it feels like for us to look at you or even glance at you on command, let alone hold your gaze as you speak to us.

I have found the various techniques used to "teach" us eye contact to be very interesting. They vary from one therapy to the next, one therapist to the next and most interesting, each parent to the next. I know you long to be connected to your child, pupil or autistic client/patient in this intimate, social way, and I get that. But forcing it will rarely work. We'll do the minimum required to get relief from you and the pressure, if we are even capable at the time!

I had a birthday party once when I was about four or five years old. We were riding a train because I was still in my *Thomas the Train* phase. Mom and Dad rented a car of the train for my party. I remember feeling so bad for my friend because each time Mom would say something to him, his dad would basically grab his son's face in his hands and literally turn his head toward

Mom. Then he'd say, "look at her when she speaks to you," with anger energy behind his voice. And guess what, my friend never looked at Mom. His eyes always looked downward.

Do you realize that many of us use our peripheral vision differently than you? Sometimes it's easier for us to process visual information that way. There could be a number of reasons for it. Soma Mukhopadhyay (*RPM*) and Lenae Crandall (my *RPM* teacher) know much more about that (see reference section). When I was younger, I had a hard time looking and listening to someone at the same time. And most often, because of that, people assumed I wasn't listening just because I wasn't looking at them. There's proof right there, because I was listening to everything and basically remember everything that was said in front of me. We can listen without looking, and we are!

When I was in school where that was required a lot, it was really hard for me. I wanted to tell the teacher that I can listen or look, but I can't do both at the same time right now. Also, at home, Mom was working on two-step directions with me that one of my therapies was requiring. It also required eye contact. Would it surprise you to know that it took a couple of years for me to accomplish this, given this new information? It's just something to think about. Our sensory systems change as we age so wouldn't it be possible that goals like that may be appropriate a little later? Maybe the two-step direction goal could be accomplished by hearing the instruction only, while saving the eye contact stimulation component for later, if at all.

I know my mom was happy to learn about the different learning channels (auditory, visual, kinesthetic and tactile) and how to tell which ones were strongest and when they were available for learning. It's in *Soma's* first book (see reference section again). If you can learn about this, then teaching us everything in our life becomes easier, less stressful and much more successful in shorter amounts of time. Yeah! We all win! Happy reading.

CHAPTER SEVEN

Food Glorious Food

Food will become a dichotomy for most of us as we descend into autism and lose control of ourselves and everything else. We need it to survive, but it becomes an untamed animal. Suddenly, Mom was told that everything I loved to eat was bad for me. Not only was it bad, it was hurting me. My experience is that some of this is true during certain times in development. "But really, Mom, did you have to stop everything at once?" The pantry went, in one day, from "food-a-plenty" to a vacant cavern not worthy of my time for its exploration. I knew where the gluten-laden bread was hidden in the garage, stored safely for Dad who refused to see the culinary beauty in the nine-dollar per loaf, imported from Florida, gluten-free bread.

The "untamed animal" reference comes from food being a comfort one minute to a bland beast the next. Face it, you are all like me on this topic. Aha! You are partially autistic! Welcome to the club. If you've ever been on a diet of some sort or imposed restrictions on yourself for some reason, you can feel my pain.

I agree that this was an important move for me as a three-year-old. But, as I matured and my system healed through various interventions, Mom listened to my plea for energy work, (communicating at age eleven and a half through a letter board using *SOMA RPM*). I can now access energy to digest any food. No more nine dollar loaves of bread! I'll take sourdough, thanks!

I'd advise a more humane way, to gently eliminate one offender food at a time. This way, your beloved banshee boy or girl won't notice quite as much. "Goodbye all things white that comfort me. Hello green things, which will take a while for me to welcome as real food." Don't worry about what your child will eat in the future, for the only time is now. Stop projecting years ahead. But if you do, know you can paint any picture you want about the future because it's an exciting mystery that hasn't happened yet.

CHAPTER EIGHT

Courage and Confidence

So, as you're reading this, are you an autistic person or are you raising one? Perhaps neither! Maybe you're enamored with us for some reason or you're "studying us," as we are such different types of humans. I like that you're intrigued enough to read my book, as I've got some unique and some might say, "shocking" perspective to share with you from my "first class seat" on the autism airline.

Ok, let's have it, "What's so courageous about being autistic, you want to know?" I'm glad you asked! It's not just like being in a foreign country where the language is different. It's more like being on an entirely different planet! Where's the oxygen? Is there enough for my journey? I look at all of you neuro-typicals and wonder why it's so easy for all of you to walk, keep your balance, feel your body? People don't see autistics as courageous; instead they look at the "can't do's" of autism. You neuro-typicals are able to send messages to your body and control it. You filter the noises; ignore the universal sounds and messages that constantly come. You are able to learn to communicate with words while being oblivious to other means of communicating. That is gigantic to us. And to top it off we are often out here alone. I have parents who love me to the best of their ability and stayed with me. But I have seen too often, that one or even both of the parents is not able to keep up the challenge. Someone high-tails it out of the house, town, city, state, marriage or find some other means of getting off the amusement park ride autism has created in their lives.

The parent left behind says to himself or herself, "What the heck? Now what do I do?" Their journey takes a new turn. The parent who left will learn lessons of their own, rest assured. I can tell you that once autism arrives in your life, its lessons never abandon you. So don't worry if you're the one who left for the hills. You still get to learn your lessons. I'm just glad you're reading this book. Welcome!

Now, back home to the parent left to raise us, congratulations! Yeah! Yippee! We chose *you* for a reason! You actually may not know it, but you chose us, too. It was an agreement made with God as the arbitrator. Call God "the Universe, Energy, Fate," whatever you like. They're all the same things just called something different. Please use whichever word has special meaning to you. As a parent you may question your decision once in a while, most often when we are teaching you your biggest lessons. Trust me, we question ourselves during our lessons, too. We're all just humans, after all.

These life lessons are taught in various school settings. Talk about bravery! Mom's favorite classroom was the floor of *Whole Foods*, at 5:30pm, in the produce section right in front of the sliding glass door. There is no way around it, you have to use it to enter. I had a hard time with sliding doors. Well, I found this spot to be quite an effective place to teach, more like an auditorium, of sorts. Not only did I have Mom as a faithful and committed student, but others soon got to join my class as well, tuition free!

In the "typical" world, one must save up for college, apply for scholarships, pay for books, not to mention, apply for acceptance. My classes, and those of my very esteemed colleagues on the autism spectrum, however, are free! Best of all, they take place in mobile classrooms and where we do not discriminate in our enrollment poli-cies. All are welcome to attend. Also, we can handle huge class loads, so bring your friends.

Should I show my true self yet in this book? I guess that if I am going to ask myself this question, this is the preferred chapter in which to ask it.

Courage and confidence is required by anyone who chooses to reveal who they really are. But a silent, well previously silent, autistic kid runs the risk of causing an explosion. No, not a tiny fireworks in the front yard on the Fourth of July type. More like the atomic bomb in your bedroom type. Things are "just so" one minute, while life long beliefs and assumptions disintegrate in the next. I am talking, of course, to you; parents and loved ones of autistics. My mom, as most parents of autistics, was quickly thrust into not caring what anyone thought of her. She learned that I needed soothing. She was so in tune with me. She would tune out all other people on that floor at the grocery store to be there for me, because I was in complete distress. Complete overwhelm. My mom eventually learned to let go of what people think of her or us and completely focus on loving me and telling me I was safe. This is one of the big lessons we bring to the planet, love is stronger than judgment.

When I began getting open-ended conversation with my mom, I had to strategize my self-revealing. Would you believe I laid awake at night planning this, so as not to send my innocent, unsuspecting parents to the funny farm thinking they were conversing with an alien, or to the emergency room with a heart issue! I must give them credit, as I have laid some really heavy stuff on them. They thought they were raising a non-verbal kid who was smart but was trapped inside a vacant world of his own. Instead, I shocked them with some zingers. This is my first expression of who I really am:

The topic of self-acceptance is a hard one. Who knows their true self? I think autistics do. I am not getting stronger by making myself happy communicating more with words, but I am with spelling. I am just me. I do my best to change. I try to talk, but out comes nonsense. Someday this will change. I got no more problems than you do, but mine are worse. That is why I see Jesus sometimes. He loves us. I know that. I have seen much more but I don't think it's good to tell. So, the thing to know is love God and your neighbor. That way, you have to be one with God. That way you're yourself. The end.
("Written" through the *RPM* letter board on May 5, 2015.)

I communicated a lot, prior to this, it's just that they didn't always notice. I wasn't just smart, but amazingly gifted. Please know that when I refer to my amazing gifts, I know they are just so, gifts, and give thanks to God for them. They did not come from me, for I am only human.

I revealed slowly, my relationship with God and Christ. I believe there's another book on that topic alone. My political views continue to escape out of my finger! I also love to share knowledge about energy. There were stories told of my experiences with school and some people who cared for me, which were very hard for my parents to hear.

I love my parents. They really wear superhero costumes, returning from battle, a little beat up and tired. They did, after all, just save the life of their kid. Talk again about courage, Mom and Dad risked everything for me. Did you know they didn't leave me overnight with anyone else for the first eight years of my life? I always had one of them with me for comfort. That meant no date weekends or adult boring trips winetasting, antiquing or whatever. They always had me in tow. They had to import Papa and Grandma from Minnesota to hang with me when they went to *Son-Rise* training for a week in Massachusetts.

We didn't go out to dinner at all the first three years after my diagnosis. I was on every diet known to man and tended to voice my opinion regarding the unfair treatment of me when it came to food. Gluten-free, casein-free, nut-free, low-oxalate, sugar-free, preservative-free, organic only, oh, and nothing artificial.

"What's the point of meals?" I asked in my sarcastic, stubborn, high-pitched banshee voice. "Surely that stuff is okay to eat. Look how many people do and how readily available it is!" Ha! We have a long battle ahead of us to change society's views on food and healthy farming. Anyway, it was brave of my parents to forgo social engagements, which centered on food I couldn't eat. Some of their friends faded away, others took a hiatus and returned when my parents could be more social, and still others settled for hamburgers on the grill and just hanging out and enjoying each other's company. My screams during dinner did not scare the most steadfast of friends; you know who you are.

Gifts aren't always wrapped up with a bow. Sometimes they're flipping burgers on the grill with Mom and Dad, and full of hugs.

So, we know it takes courage and confidence to raise one of us, especially since most often, God surprises those lucky parents. Parents don't often dream of, imagine, and pray for their child to become autistic. Did you? I guess you should write to me if you did. I'd love to know why and also ask you which planet you're from! I'll just say this, it's one thing to raise us and quite another to *be* us.

It's easy in this world, to often forget the other person's perspective in any given situation. I believe that all (or at least most) autistics would agree with me when I say that we don't always have in mind *your* situation. Especially when we get overwhelmed, over-stimulated, frustrated or so worn out by the millions of hours of therapy you put us through so as not to let us drift off into our own world, or as Mom called it, Autismland. I think if you really analyze yourselves a little closer, you have a need to drift off, too. Can you remember a time when you did today? Where were you and why did you space out? Who forced you back into reality or to be present, as they say in Autismland? Maybe it was even you! How did the person do it? How did you feel inside when they did?

Now imagine you had a long day at work and you had the pleasure of commuting home with thousands of other hard working people, inching along at the rush hour warp speed of ten miles per hour. All you cared about was getting home, sitting in your comfy couch watching the Sports Channel or some home improvement show. But your spouse, kids or perfect strangers kept showing up in your line of sight demanding your attention. You verbal show off's (ha-ha) can just let it rip; "move please," "I'm too tired to play a family game, I just need to relax," "I need some 'me' time first, then I'll play," the list goes on.

Well, what about us? Do you think we're that different from you? School, PT, OT, social skills classes, speech, swimming lessons, *RPM* lessons, gymnastics, music lessons and billions of other therapies. Considering that just processing everyday sounds and sights are a hundred times harder for us, please know that we're tired and stressed, we need downtime, too. So, if we express our disdain with outbursts or physical stuff, please see it as a form of communication, not a behavior that needs to be "extinguished." Granted, I don't blame you for your emotional upheaval during our teachings. But if you don't see us as having some of the same needs you have, you leave us no choice but to be "explosively expressive." Yes, feel free to use that term in your IEP's (Individualized Education Plans), as I have not patented it.

Courage and determination come from within each of us. You can also ask God to give you more of it. It's like shopping at the grocery store. Fill your cart up with whatever you want. God's Safeway is free! Confidence has always been yours. Just focus on what feels good in your body. It's called by some, intuition.

CHAPTER NINE

A Want Is Better Than
A Need

Let's listen to ourselves talk. The words we choose are so important. We often say, we "need" this or we "need" that. Do we really? Will we cease to exist without it? Well, if we look at life in reality, all we need to survive as humans are food (actually, very little) and water. Shelter is also needed in many parts of the world. After those things, Baloo says it best in *The Jungle Book*, "the simple bare necessities of life." Everything else is just icing on the cake. So, let's take a listen, shall we? "I need more money, I need a vacation, I need to relax, I need to lose 30 pounds." Then there's the parents of autistics saying, "we need to get him into this doctor, he needs more speech, she needs friends, we need some respite, we need to make a plan because we won't live forever," etc. You see, no mention of food, water or shelter in any of those statements. It's interesting that Webster defines the word "need" in three ways:

> 1. A situation in which someone or something must do or have something

> 2. Something that a person must have: something that is needed in order to live or succeed or be happy

> 3. A strong feeling that you must have or do something

I guess Dad's right when he says it depends on the mindset of the person. So, if a drug addict thinks he needs drugs to be happy or to cope, that's very powerful, as his brain (conscious mind) is giving a direct order to his subconscious (the order taker and follower) that the drug is a need for survival. If this postulate is true, then wow, we are so powerful!

Beware about deciding things are a "need." It puts an actual demand out there to the universe, God or whatever you believe drives you in this life. But, if we put things out there as wants or desires, it's a much more gracious approach. It's almost like saying, "Thank you for providing me the necessities. I really appreciate them. Now, as I learn my lessons, I'd like this or that. Thank you for your gifts that continuously flow to me. I will use them wisely and share the abundance."

Okay, now let's look at this through the

affectionately blurred lens of the average autism parent. "I just need to be able to hug my child." Do you? To want that, heck yes! To need that is a mindset that places so much pressure on us. There are a number of reasons we may not be huggers at any given time.

Maybe our skin hurts to be touched. When I had a high oxalate count, it felt like shards of glass were right under the surface of my skin. I could withstand gentle hugs and I could withstand more on my back than my front. I gave backward hugs or side hugs. Mom was usually gentle, so I could ease into cuddles with her. And it helped that she was soft. Mom may not like being "soft," but let me tell you, it worked for me, and still does. Note: Lighten up on yourself, Mom. You are beautiful.

Another reason we may not hug is that you are asking for them at times when we just don't feel like emotionally hugging you, or anyone else. Do you ever give the obligatory hug? Come on now, we've all done it, maybe to distant relatives at holiday gatherings, for example? Please don't force us to do that, by the way. We don't know their energy. They're often uneasy around us anyway, so their energy is hesitant. And holidays are enough for us to process anyway; schedules can change, crowds appear, noise levels increase, there's crazy running around, excess cleaning, etc. (or is that just my house?). I've surmised otherwise over the years, even though I don't live with you.

My point is that if you wait patiently for us to come to you, we will! And, it will be from deep within us, not obligatory in nature. Which do you prefer, a Hallmark card purchased at the store with somebody else's sentiment written on it and signed by your loved one? Or, would you prefer the hand written note with words chosen especially for you, even if written on a sheet of white, lined paper? The former is easy...run in, buy it and run out. The latter requires thought, patience and an inner desire to create and express. Please remember, we do not see every social grace the same way you may see it. We have human emotional needs like you do, but we are not societal conformists like so many of you are in this world.

All of these things may contribute to our willingness or ability to give hugs at any given time; my state of mind/your state of mind, our energy level/your energy level, our flexibility, our physical sensitivity, our emotional desire, your emotional need of us, or our disdain of constantly being told what to do or not do.

So, try this for a while; get down on our level (depending on our stature) and just fling your arms wide open as an invitation to us. We'll either come to you willingly, or not. And do not take offense if we don't. It may be an invitation to you to check your own emotional state or may be a lesson for you in learning that we just aren't ready for some reason, and that's okay! It's not an insult. It just is. We will feel your disappointment, so don't think you can hide it. Just don't choose to create it. You can really transform inside to a place of understanding, compassion and growth.

I am always prepared, in case
I "want" some food.

CHAPTER TEN

Hey Teacher I Don't Get It

When parents need something from a child, it's a little different for us, especially because we love you and want you to be happy. But if you choose to see us as teachers, a lot more sense will be made from our actions. Learning is a life-long adventure for each of us. Yet, there are an amazing number of adults who don't understand that or won't admit it. Sure, it's a given in this society that kids go to school for at least twelve years to learn the basics of our western education: Math, science, history, English, a little bit of music and art (but sadly, not enough anymore). Did you know music and art affect our brains in some amazing ways? I feel like my brain tingles when I play the piano. I know it takes many neurons to fire and work together to get one of my musical masterpieces from the written note on the page, through my brain and out my fingers to the specific black and ivory keys.

I wasn't always able to process musical sounds, especially during the beginning of my autism journey. But now I can, thanks to hundreds of hours of *Masgutova* work, primarily. Anyway, back to my point about education. In many a thought process, we learn through high school, maybe college, then we get a job, hopefully in our chosen field. There will of course, be a small learning curve there, too, but then, voila! Most adults think the learning is over and it's smooth sailing down easy street. Then they have kids and are expected to do the teaching, not necessarily the learning. Been there, done that.

Ha! No wonder we autistics come as such a shock to our families and friends. We are not hanging out on Easy Street. In fact, that location can't even be found in our GPS system, so don't waste your time entering it. Not that raising a neuro-typical kid is easy, as I'm sure that's got it's own challenges. But trust me, we stretch the limits of our parent's boundaries: emotionally, physically, financially and educationally. We'll also see how creative you are when it comes to getting things done like acquiring services for us, finding specialists, therapists, finding special schools and teachers. Oh, and once you do find these people, in as classy a way as possible, assertively finding a way to get us an appointment sooner than six months from now. See, you begin your education with us, just when you thought you were beginning your stroll down Easy Street.

Our first appearance as educators is when we are little innocent bundles of inspiration. We may be "screamy" and perplexing, but way down deep, we are inspiring you. Do you find that to be an interesting choice of words, "inspiring?" I understand that for many parents, that may not be the first choice of words that pops into their head as we're screaming out of control for no apparent reason. When we do things like rocking back and forth, twirling a string, throwing rocks, flapping our hands or even hitting ourselves, it's a very serious activity. Believe it or not we are inspiring you, I promise. We're inspiring you to look deep within yourselves to find new ways of acquiring inner peace and creative, out-of-the-box ways to help us. Also, to develop more patience than you ever thought one person could have, to open your hearts wider than ever before and find ways to totally accept us for who we are, today. Not when we talk or when we stop screaming or exhibiting "inappropriate" social behaviors, but right now.

But, what happens when the student doesn't realize that he/she is a student? That may require an intervention. I don't mean it in the sense of an alcoholic or anything, rather more like a rescuing. Sometimes an awakening is necessary for the teaching to take place. As I've said before in my life, the door cannot be opened if no one is awake inside to unlock it. We cannot teach those who are unwilling to learn. You can have tons of knowledge to share, but one can't share it if there's no one listening. I guess that begs the question, "If a non-verbal autistic kid shouts messages in the woods, but no one listens, is there really a message at all?" Let's see, maybe it was really, "if a tree falls in the forest and there's no one around to hear it, does it make a sound?" or something like that. You get the point, right?

So, how does the autistic kid/mentor acquire students for his class? Especially those innately brilliant close ones named Mom, Dad, Brother, Sister, Grandma, Grandpa, Aunt, Uncle and Cousin? Brilliant? Yes. But sometimes they are not as open and available for learning. Not as often as you'd really hope.

Why would a student enroll in a class taught by someone from a different planet who is not fluent in their native tongue? Sounds like a daunting experience, doesn't it? Why take that class when the classes down the hall are taught by English-speaking teachers, whose walls are draped with diplomas and certificates in medicine, psychology, behavioral science or education?

Where are the diplomas of the non-English-speaking "alien" teachers? I personally await the day when we, too, shall be donned with the heavy-weighted paper, but which does not call loudly to others, "Hey, you can listen to me and trust my advice, for I have read many books and studied the writings of others who have read many books! I have reached conclusions based on subjects (people with autism) who were put to scientific tests and prodded to answer in a singular, mainstream way, far different from their natural way of expression."

No, instead ours would shout, "I have these diplomas because of my firsthand experience in my specialty: Autism Spectrum Disorder. I have completed, thus far, 117,000 hours of my 'practicum,' all using personal experiences. I have gathered billions of terabytes of information based on observation of neuro-typicals. I have painstakingly compared data collected during this life-long experiment called 'Living on this Earth.' I do not waiver on my findings and there is no one who will ever be able to prove said findings incorrect. For I am an unbiased explorer, paid by no one except God. My reimbursement comes in the form of unconditional love, understanding, comfort and strength. Since I am the only me, I am the only expert on me. Would I ever claim to know why you act a certain way, or feel a certain way during an experience? And my favorite, would I claim to understand your level of intelligence by merely watching your bodily movements or listening to sounds emitted from your vocal chords, neither of which you have control over 100% of the time?" Absolutely not! Sorry Sigmund.

Okay, maybe all of that on one diploma paper may be slightly excessive. Maybe it would only say, "Happy Autism Aficionado." The rest would be implied as society shifts from judgmental, ego-based thinking to open-minded acceptance. Change is coming, as more and more students enroll in our classes. Some may enroll willingly, while others may be dragged to class, kicking and screaming. Then, there is the amazing group of students who join unwillingly, but transform from the inside out and become experts of themselves. They are the real change-makers, top of the class. And best of all, they achieve the coveted status of "Teacher's Pet." The best of the best! They are awarded with affection, respect, hugs, knowledge and the most sought after reward of all, the crème de la crème, inner peace on their continued journey.

So, are you a student yet? May I see your

proof of registration please? Hahaha, just kidding. I'd never require any proof of registration or pre-requisites. Energy created between us will lay the groundwork.

We thank you for showing up, even though an advanced degree wasn't in your plan. Surprise! Now you get to decide whether to enjoy the surprise or get upset because you're not really a surprise type of person. Either way, we're here and in your life. The only decision to make is how happy you want to be.

Opening up to our teaching will dramatically change you, but I promise that in the end, when your eyes are opened wide, the view will be more beautiful than you could have imagined. Your growth won't come without challenges, though. Nothing worth anything is easy. Have you heard the saying, "When God closes one door, He opens another, but it can be hell in the hallway?" Just know that He's with you every step of the way. Find your way through the hallway by talking to other autism parents. Those parents you look up to. Those who have found their inner peace and drive to always further their relationship with us. They are your best resource. Find a kid who is generally happy and befriend his/her parents. Hang out with people who lift you up, you needn't do all the lifting. Are you ready? Dare to learn. Dare to open up. Dare to become who you're meant to be. I'll be waiting for you with an "A"!

"Listen, learn, then teach. Love is the message. Live it, share it, receive it, learn it in different ways from unexpected sources, then show the world that you love God through your actions and life. That's all you need to know and everything else falls in line!"

Matteo Musso

CHAPTER ELEVEN

My Dinner Is Cold

How long does the dinnertime last at your house? Mom and Dad eat their dinner in about ten minutes. At Boy Scout camp this summer, I observed the average teenage boy taking about 15 to 20 minutes. They kicked us out of the dining hall after twenty minutes, so I'm sure that was inspiring. More on that in a minute. Did you know we were made to graze all day on small amounts of food as opposed to eating bigger meals less often? Well, we are.

Everyone complains about eating too much at Thanksgiving dinner because the food tastes so good. How do you feel afterward? Bloated (wear elastic pants if you choose to continue this "behavior"), sort of sick, lethargic, tired? Many autistics have sensitive digestive issues, so this feeling of "Thanksgiving tummy topsy-turvy" is magnified by ten or one hundred times for us, just like everything else we experience on this Earth compared to you guys. But we experience it a lot, not just on holidays.

Do your kids act different after a meal? If so, many parents, along with their doctors, may assume it is the actual food that's causing the changes. Maybe it is, sometimes. But I'd propose an alternative theory for consideration. Have you ever tried eating just two bites of something then walking away? Or, only present a tiny portion of food if you have an OCD creature like me, who has a difficult time moving on with his life if there's food left on his plate. Give two bites worth every half hour or so and you will see drastic changes in your body and energy level.

Now, I can hear all of you saying how crazy this is, how this is impossible to implement at work for yourselves or at school for your kids. It's definitely different than what you're used to but that doesn't render something impossible! If making that change could drastically affect your health by giving your body a constant energy source, eliminating stress put on your digestive system, speeding up your metabolism and by staying more alert, would it be worth a try?

Maybe it's three to four bites an hour instead of the 30-minute option, but never more than an hour without new energy entering your body. You can always excuse yourself from a meeting for a personal break. People will assume you

need to use the restroom, but you can eat something instead. Sometimes their misguided
assumptions can come in handy! This type of
thing can be written into IEP's, too. Sure, the
education team will be so excited to implement
this, but it's as important and serious to many of
us as medicine. Acid reflux, indigestion, bowel
movements, bloating, tiredness, "spaciness" and
much more can all be positively affected by this
way of eating.

You can actually spend *more* quality time as a
family by doing this, too. By eating the evening
meal over a two hour time period, you get two
hours together instead of twenty minutes. So,
what would that look like? First, you eat your
salad, then disburse to play a quick game or talk
about something. Thirty minutes later, the
protein source is ready. Eat a couple bites then
cover it with foil and put it back in the oven to
keep warm. If you're having a side dish, add a
bite of that, too. For example, roast beef and
mashed potatoes. Then disburse again to finish
your game or do a bit of homework. Or, watch
an episode of *Big Bang Theory*. Thirty minutes
later, you pull your plate out of the oven and
finish. You get the idea. Nothing is impossible.

Remember when I said that we stretch your
creativity? This is a perfect example. Creativity
doesn't always relate to art. It's a part of every

aspect of your life.

Cows and horses, notice how they eat? They graze. They're huge animals, which require a consistent intake of nutrition. Do you think we could learn from a horse? It's said that their gait mimics that of humans more than any other animal. That's why kids with special motor and emotional needs find riding horses to be so therapeutic. Ahh! So we *can* learn from these animals. Why stop learning at their gait? Maybe their eating habits are worth a look, too. I think we can learn a lot if we open our minds, not to see what *is*, but rather, what *can be*.

Now I promised to tell you more about eating at Boy Scout Camp. In case you've never been one, I'll tell you that no moss grows under the feet of Boy Scouts. They seem to have a lot to do and are constantly moving. The epitome of my theory was displayed at summer camp. But first, you should know that I am naturally a culinary grazer. I always have been, but it seems more important now that I'm a little older. Did you know that I ate gluten-free pizza every day for two years when I was younger? I was more of a food snob back then, very picky and controlling, too. We all know that any food issue can be related to texture or control. Self-esteem enters into other food disorders, but not so much with us. Control is a biggie, but flexibility is another.

But I maintain that control and flexibility are related.

Understand that for me, meals don't really exist. Breakfast blends into lunch, which blends into dinner, which blends into bed! That's how I roll. I need to digest food as it comes into me. Boy Scouts, apparently, don't do that. Perhaps they'd like to, if given the opportunity. But not at camp, that's for sure! I must admit that Mom and I were both in a bit of shock the first day at camp. In an instant, my dietary world spun out of control when Big Joe, the dining hall boss, told us in no uncertain terms, that we had just five minutes to finish our breakfast. My heart leapt into my throat. I had no choice. No, I didn't eat faster, it was instant paralysis! Then came the heavy feeling of pressure. What was I going to do? I couldn't throw away the food on my plate. What did it do to be rendered useless and unwanted? I would surely need it in the hours to come. Mom strategically grabbed many napkins, wrapped up the food and delicately shoved it into my backpack. It is a challenge to "delicately shove" something, but Mom is gifted like that. So, off to our first class we ran, food-laden napkins in tow. A huge lesson learned, and it was only the first official hour of camp!

All it took was a strategy during the rest of the meals at camp. I understood the tight schedule of classes and just needed to make a plan which would accommodate my digestive schedule and the camp schedule. And we did, that's Creativity!

Mom understands my digestive requirements so she is never embarrassed to explain to others why I need to eat throughout the day, even if no one else is eating. If I need to take a breakfast bar into church and quietly eat it, what's the biggie? Some others eat cough drops with the loudest wrappers in the world, so what's wrong with my silent Nutrigrain bar? Nothing. It's as innocent as the morning sun.

Cheers to the food that sustained me for
two solid years. I still love you!

CHAPTER TWELVE

It's Not Really Food Anymore

Why do you think God is making so many autistics with food allergies or intolerances? Not only us, but kids in general. Then add in asthma and skin irritations, all happening to young, innocent beings who have had nothing to do with the situations causing these conditions, but are merely the recipients of the effects. Let's see; could there be a correlation between these health epidemics and polluting our Earth? Close your eyes now if you don't want to hear the answer. Absolutely my friends!

I asked Mom how many other kids have food allergies, so we looked it up on the internet. To quote FARE (Food Allergy Research and Education), "Researchers estimate that up to 15 million Americans have food allergies. This potential disease affects 1 in 13 children under the age of 18 years old, that's roughly two in every classroom. The economic cost of children's food allergies is nearly $25 billion per year."

Wow! Can you believe it? I have yet to meet or be around any autistic kid who isn't currently on some special diet or hasn't been on one in the past. Most autism families go organic, non-GMO and don't allow artificial anything in their food. Isn't it strange to have to pay more for food just because you don't want to eat poison in it? When God created Earth, it was ready to sustain human life. Then humans decided that mass-producing for bigger profits was more important than the purity of our food, water and air.

"We have billions of people to feed on this planet, so we must find cheaper ways to produce food," some would say. I'm no mathematician (oh wait, yes I am), but if society would admit that this "food pollution" was the cause of so much disease and illness, the money saved on medicine, doctor bills and pharmaceutical research to develop new drugs to help us cope with the effects of these poisons, would be trillions of dollars! That money could re-enter the economy in the form of pure farming, clean energy sources and feeding the world.

Can you imagine a world without hunger or disease? It's possible, I assure you. But it would take a tsunami of awareness, motivation and willingness to change. Enter autistics. We are here as the silent (or not so silent in many cases) awareness. Verbal kids who have these issues (all kids, not just autistics) can tell their parents their tummy hurts, or whatever. Non-verbal's can't. Therefore, we often go through our day in pain and get in trouble for acting out, making too many noises and being disruptive. We go through so much and so do our parents, just to bring some attention to this issue. It's a very hard lesson to teach because so many people and groups don't want to acknowledge or admit it. Many neuro-typical parents accept the kid's allergies as "just the way it is," but I suggest that the silent autistics are shouting a message loud and clear, "CLEAN UP THE EARTH!" It doesn't *have* to be this way. It didn't start out this way; man's free will made it this way. Sometimes the loudest messages have the quietest messengers.

I might write to Heaven about this issue, to apologize that people are disrespecting this beautiful Earth. Together, we can purify our food, water and air. All we have to do is *stop* doing some things and *start* doing others. Can you imagine?

The more of us that paint this beautiful image in our minds, the sooner it will come to fruition.

Ready, set, imagine!

CHAPTER THIRTEEN

Getting Creative

I promised earlier that you would grow as a person if you hang out with us. But if you're raising us, you also get to become an artist, of sorts. I mentioned earlier, that creativity isn't found exclusively in traditional art forms such as drawing, painting and sculpting. Raising us and getting us the services we need has become it's own art form and you get to learn how to sculpt.

Did you sign up online in your sleep for this special training? You did, my friends. You just don't really remember. So, here's the syllabus for our class on becoming a "service recipient," a "therapy beast," and a juggler of schedules and time itself. Are you excited?

Now some of you may have previously taken classes that claimed to help with these things, but we'll see if they actually did.

Class 1: The Diagnosis

Did the doctor or psychologist come toward you, after the four grueling hours of testing your child, with a long face and a sad compassionate look as if delivering the worst news in the world? "Your child is autistic," they say. If they did (and they did with my mom, I remember that day all too well), you probably responded like a mirror of that professional. Did your heart sink or stop for a while? Did you lose your breath, as if someone stole your oxygen? Did you cry as if Niagra Falls had been moved from New York to your tear ducts and eye sockets? If your reaction was similar to any of these scenarios, I don't blame you. It's a natural human response to news delivered encapsulated in the judgment of sadness, distress, challenge or negativity. And why wouldn't it be delivered that way? After all, who in their right mind would like a child to lose their ability to speak or never acquire it in the first place? What kind of crazy person would be excited if the child developed the uncanny ability to stack blocks up and knock them down for hours at a time? Who appreciates that the child makes strange utterances as if speaking "Venution" (the native tongue on the planet Venus)? What person enjoys hearing that their entire life and the lives of their family members is taking a whole new direction other than the one the parents had so painstakingly planned? What exactly did you learn in this class?

Class 2: Creativity 101, Becoming an Autism Artist

We all know that really cool artists wear really cool hats. Let's notice a few different types. Each style is unique and expresses something different.

• *The Parent Hat*: It has a pointed tip. The information goes in through the tip and expands as the information explodes into possibility.

• *The Medical Doctor Hat*: It opens at the top so that academic, scientific and medical knowledge can blend with universal energy (spiritual or whatever you want to call it).

• *The Psychology Hat*: It's really more like a visor, when worn by the Autism Artist. It blocks out the most harmful factors yet allows light and vision to shine forth. This hat is able to affect more families than most other hats, as psychology is the field of science under which autism has been placed. This hat MUST be worn with caution.

• *The Playful Occupational Therapy Hat*: Those who enjoy getting down on the floor and playing joyfully with us should wear this hat. It is a very creative hat, full of vibrant colors and happy energy. This hat has a very wide brim, as it is used to cast a large shadow over the fact that the play is actually a therapy to help us.

• *The Physical Therapy Hat.* This one can be as fun as the OT hat, but it's a little, or a lot, heavier. The wearer of this hat has the challenge of helping our uncooperative bodies obey our brains. The artist will recognize the need to approach this from the inside out. This artist often consults with Dr. Svetlana Masgutova. OT's and speech therapists do, too. This brings us to our next hat.

• *The Speech Therapy Hat:* Once it's established that we can move our mouths and make sounds, it's time to change the shape of this hat. It's a baseball hat, facing forward during the time of discovery. If we have the motor capability to speak, then the hat must be turned around, opening to the entire world of self-expression and unique ways of communication. The artist understands that we constantly communicate through means other than just the spoken word. If we do not yet have the motor control of our mouths, lips and tongue, this hat-wearer gets to apply the skills of their education in a more technical way first.

Parents become artists themselves when influenced by these other autism artists. The "power of the coat"(white coat that doctor's wear) has great influence, so I pray the coat owners respect it. They have a huge effect on the journey of a family with autism. Parents seek guidance, but from what source? That is the million dollar question.

Class 3: The Services

State-funded Social Services. You may wonder why I even know this term at my age. Well, since I turned thirteen yesterday, I am a teenager and privy to such knowledge. Ha! Truth is, I've heard the "struggle" conversations my entire life. Parents go to coffee and bring us, with trusty Ipad in tow, not knowing that we absorb every consonant, vowel, syllable, sentence and paragraph spoken. Since my mom talks to many parents as she tries to help them, I've had the unique opportunity to eavesdrop my little ears off during the past six years or so. Happy to have had that open and honest conversation, be it one-sided, of course. I just took it all in, like my autistic colleagues do on a daily basis, not knowing that someday I'd have an opportunity to write this book and shout from my mountaintop in a language understood by all. The truth is that no person is superior to another just because they can talk or have control over their body.

We do need help acclimating to this world. Therapeutic services are essential. But I caution you, make no mistake that autism is a business. While I understand and respect the need to make money, enough is enough. When I heard my parents discussing the amount of money they were spending on different therapies, it really made me sick to my stomach. And you all think our stomach issues are only food related. No way!

Some therapies claim to require thirty hours a week and can only be implemented by trained professionals. Oh, my goodness. There's another book on my experience training these "professionals" alone. I'm sorry. I believe there are many people out there who truly want to help us but who just get sucked into the vortex of this therapy which claims to understand us, but has a lot to learn about us. Some parts of this therapy are closer to the truth than others, but many parents are not educated in the differences. This therapy has become a money-making wild beast. Hours and hours spent telling us what to do and when to do it. Little attention is paid to our communications. They are categorized and judged as appropriate or inappropriate, right or wrong.

We are not computers which need to be programmed or pets needing to be trained to respond. We are fully functional human beings who process information uniquely and struggle to communicate through a single, limited way; spoken language. Does that justify hours spent on deciding what is considered furniture and what isn't? What is considered school supplies and what isn't?

It's funny to consider the deaf person or the hearing impaired. They often cannot enunciate clearly the spoken word, yet they are not immediately assumed unintelligent or cognitively delayed. They are taught ASL (American Sign Language) and many are trained in that new language. In fact, isn't it considered a foreign language in schools now? What about *RPM*? Can't that be considered like sign language? Let's see; the user doesn't speak cohesively...check. There are few trained interpreters of the special language...check. The cognitive function of the non-speaker is intact...check. They have other senses heightened to make up for the deficit of another (ex: a blind person's sense of hearing is heightened to make up for the deficit in sight) ...check.

Which of our senses are heightened, you ask? Not only our ability to read your body language, but our sense of your energy, your mood, your attitude, your true belief about something, your confidence in our abilities and your overall attitude toward us as people. All of this comes natural to us. So when you feel like someone's picking on you at work or rush hour traffic has paralyzed you, don't bring it home. We may feel obligated to turn teacher on you, to help you see that what's important now is family time and that you can have a wonderful evening if you choose it.

Okay, I digressed a bit. I tend to do that because so much is stored up in my head. Back to the part about acquiring services. What therapies do we need? That question will be answered individually by each one of us. You know the saying, "If you've met one person with autism, you've met one person with autism." That statement couldn't be truer. I need certain ones and my friends need others. But there are a plethora of commonalities, too. (Plethora is one of my Mom's favorite words. So I'll use it, too)

Class 3.5: Respite, It's Important

Wherever you live, in the USA at least, there are services available to help you help us. Have you heard of them? They are paid for by the states and are the best kept secrets. Everyone deserves them but only the most "sleuthy" and most creatively persistent parents receive them. Decide that you want help in an area or two, decide that it's out there somewhere, and then find it. The creativity lies in your mindset.

Why is this important? Because, when parents are willing to sacrifice anything for us, it comes from a love that is deeper than any sea. It is a beautiful gesture but often accompanied by stress from societal expectations like keeping your house, job, savings account, retirement, and the list goes on. Oh, and don't forget family obligations and friendship creation and upkeep.

All of these things pile up on the shoulders of our parents. While they want and lovingly choose to juggle all these balls at once for us, the dichotomy kicks in and the energy in our home shifts from joy to stress. That's pre-diagnosis joy and post-diagnosis heaviness of heart, stress of responsibility and in some cases, hopelessness. This is why you need to acquire services.

How do you think we feel during all of this? I'll give you some choices: happy, sad, tired, scared, guilty, responsible, confused, lonely, crazy? If you answered "all of the above except one of them," you get an A! You see, the thing parents don't know and don't think about is that we hear it all with our super-sonic hearing capabilities. They are exacerbated by our ability to feel your true heart, not only the part you want others to see. Please don't take this as more pressure, but rather, as an invitation and a plea from all of us to take care of yourself. If we lose our loving parent(s), the ones who believe in us, love and know us the best, to insanity, craziness, the funny farm or even depression, we are in big trouble.

Besides looking at it from a selfish point of view, it's not fair to you, either. My mom went through so much turmoil acquiring services for me: sleeplessness, weight gain (she wouldn't sacrifice time working with me for her own health), anxiety, greying hair and actual heart issues. I saw it all and even more, felt it all, for we are mirrors of you. Did you know that?

Let's say we're working or playing together fine one minute, then we have an outburst we can't control or our body does something on it's own (the auto-pilot kicks in). Then your energy changes, it's not necessarily bad, but it's a shift nonetheless. We'll react to your energy shift with our energy. Some like to label these energy shifts as "behaviors," then judge them as good or bad. If bad, they must be "extinguished." If good, they are praised or rewarded. Energy is not good or bad, it just is. Once created, it can only be transformed. It cannot be extinguished.

Imagine a stepladder with ten rungs. When everyone is chill, happy and relaxed; that's ground level. Our body decides it's time to run out the door. You will then climb the ladder. Which rung you land on depends upon where that door leads. If it's a busy street with cars zipping by; rung ten, in an instant! If it leads to a hallway in a professional office building, it could range from two to ten, depending on how you let the judgments of others affect you. If the door opens onto our back yard, maybe it's just a third rung offense, but depending on your mood and level of flexibility, it could be an eight.

Now, back to the title of this section, respite. It's kind of funny that some parents don't think they can take this time for themselves. Whoever could they trust to mind their creative and persistent little teacher? They simply need to be near their child at all times. "He needs me always," their thoughts persist.

Respite gives a caregiver a break from caring for their dependent, so they can take care of themselves. I'm not here to say that parents (usually the moms) don't need a break or that they should forfeit their respite services. On the contrary! Keep this little nugget in your pocket if you are one of those guilt-ridden parents who won't take time for yourself to rejuvenate and have some fun that doesn't include us. We may need respite from you!

I say this with all the love and gratefulness in the world. There are many reasons I say this. You need some time to relax, we all do. When you are tired, you have less patience with us (reflect on my previous statement, *we are mirrors of your energy*), therefore we have a shortage of patience for you and ourselves. That usually doesn't make for the happiest existence in our house.

We need exposure to other caring energy. What happens if we get too over-dependent on you and you suddenly disappear, you get invited to a girls weekend overnight or a dad's golf weekend? We couldn't possibly be expected to go to that extreme of being without you overnight all at once. What if you broke your hip and found yourself in a rehab center for a week? We'd go into shock! Things happen unexpectedly, so don't think you're doing us any favors by constantly being around us and forbidding others to totally be in charge of us while you are out of the house. We need this exposure to other caring energy to expand our communication skills and our flexibility. Besides, sharing the joy of us with others is nice of you. They'll get to learn their lessons, too.

You want to learn your lessons about trusting,

don't you? Trusting another person who has been thoroughly checked and vetted, of course, and trusting God and angels to keep us safe while you're gone. Even trusting your spouse with us is challenging sometimes, I hear. Mom had a hard time leaving me alone with Dad for the first few years of my autism. I remember that very well. Poor Mom! The ABA therapists had brainwashed her into thinking that if I was left alone to enjoy my block-stacking ritual, it would really hurt me. "He must stay in our world!" they'd constantly drill into the innocent and frightened brain in my mom's head, "or you'll undo all the work we've done over these past three hours!" "Yikes," she'd think. Well, that wasn't her exact sentiment, but it's the one I'll choose to write.

Please take time alone with your spouse. You two need time to do grown-up things. Sure, you could drag us along but then most of your energy will leave your spouse and land in our laps, again. Believe it or not, we realize that you had a life and relationship prior to our triumphant arrival on the scene. We know that adults enjoy different activities than kids, at least some of the time. For example, Mom and Dad enjoy wine tasting, but I find it boring. Now root beer tasting is fun for the entire family! By the way, the Schell's Brewery in New Ulm, MN is my heritage and we make the best root beer in the world! It's called 1919. It's good over vanilla ice cream, too. Yum. I'm saying, "eat the ice cream" over and over right now because I'm stuck in a loop. I'm driving Mom crazy. But she just laughs now and makes funny comments back to me, like "Never!" pronounced "nevahhhh" with verve. This helps me get out of my "ice cream loop" quickly and without stress. It's much better than letting her energy change to frustration or ignoring my communication with underlying animosity. We can feel it, you know.

Going to grown-up movies is another thing. I like Disney movies and basically, good-hearted stories. Mom and Dad do too, but sometimes our sense of humor differs. We can all agree on one thing though, the *Big Bang Theory ROCKS!* There's nothing like family bonding over watching brilliantly smart guys learning social skills and trying to get girlfriends. All the while, the show is sneaking in science facts to its unsuspecting viewers. Gotta love that, if you're a science and math-loving kid with autism!

Adult parties can be okay, but they run the risk of being too loud or boring, no offense. If that's the case, you know we have no choice but to find ways to entertain ourselves or get your attention. You guys go and have fun talking for hours. We'll be fine staying home chilling out watching a movie, stacking blocks, reading books or ripping paper. We need downtime, too. I'm sure you can find a big-hearted person to hang out with us. I must say though, that I have had an interesting social education by going to these adult parties, before Mom and Dad would leave me with other people. I'd have fun observing social behaviors and rituals. When I get done writing this book, it would be fun to share what I've observed in another book. Stay tuned to the "Teo Network!"

Class 4: Parents Need Grown-Up Time Alone

Maintaining a relationship with someone is a lot of commitment and I know this from experience over my thirteen years here. If you forget to tend to the soil, the beautiful flower can't bloom. I speak for all of the flowers in the autism garden, I think, when I say that having a loving energy in our homes between all who live there is imperative to our thriving. If you find yourself drifting away from your partner, please get some help. Living in a home filled with pain, anger, loneliness or resentment is a hundred times harder on us as we feel that energy amplified like an electric guitar at a Van Halen concert, with seats right next to the speakers!

Burying feelings simply doesn't work. We're like bloodhounds sniffing for a bone in the backyard. The scent can't be hidden from a hound and your energy and inner truth can't be hidden from us. Sniff, sniff. And, no, you can't return us to the pound. Just remember, communication skills aren't just needed by autistics; they are for everyone to enjoy.

Class 5: Flexibility

How many IEP (Individualized Education Plan) or ABA (Applied Behavioral Analysis) goals are centered on this? Can you guess how many of us would like to add flexibility goals to your IEP? I say this with a cute giggle, not a sassy sneer. Think about this for a minute, how truly flexible are you in your life? God and the Universe have actually written an IEP for each of us, you included. Most, if not all, contain a flexibility component. If you had a meeting agenda at work, were you flexible with it? When you wanted chicken for dinner and your spouse or family wanted hamburger, were you flexible? TV shows, you flexible? A certain route you drive to work, flexible? Your kid's homework versus playing, flexible in the order of them? Your political views, are you flexible? Especially not this election, it seems. You get my drift?

When we don't want to stop what we're doing in order to do something you or someone else wants us to do, we're labeled inflexible or rigid, then goals are written accordingly. What type of behavior plan shall we put in place so you will change your vote to Hillary instead of the Donald, or vice-versa? A behavior plan for my dad to consider salad as an entire meal, instead of just a course; no matter if it was two feet long and one foot deep, that would be entertaining for me to see. Write one to get a vegan-vegetarian to eat a cheeseburger! The most powerful behavior plan would be written for a person paralyzed in an accident to start using their limbs again. If that sounds crazy to you, that's because it is! We want to control ourselves but we simply can't all the time. Search for the compassion you give freely to someone trying to regain the ability to walk after that accident, and share it with us. We're trying just as hard and get just as frustrated as they do!

So what action can be taken about the bolting, you ask? Well, come and get us, for sure, but try not to panic. I doubt if many of you would let us get into unsafe predicaments anyway. Then, tell us that you understand that we don't always have control over our bodies and that you are going to help us back to our original place. If you

83

can truly feel this inside, the love energy is what we feel. That will help us regain our balance and become more grounded again. This is a totally different energy than telling us that we're behaving badly or *making you* feel scared or upset.

Remember a powerful thing that will change your life...no one has the power to *make you feel* anything. We *choose* our own feelings as a response to things that happen in our lives. The responses are based on our beliefs at the time. At *Son-Rise* training, they teach stimulus-belief-response. Mom has shared that one with me, charts and everything. Isn't that cool? So don't tell your kid, "You make me scared when you do that." That's putting the burden on us but it also makes us very powerful, too. Do you want that for your child? Do you want to give someone else control over your emotions and your feelings? Instead say, "I got scared when you ran out the door." It may sound silly to you, but it makes a huge difference to us and it gives you your power back.

Now if this persistently happens, the bolting, then it could very well be some sort of communication and you can speak to us about it in a calm, age-appropriate manner and vocabulary. Talk to us as if we are best friends out to coffee at Starbucks. Be honest and pour your heart out.

We know what's in it anyway, so if you try to cover it up, the trust and respect diminishes. If you are open and honest with us and choose to assume we understand everything you say and feel (even if we are pre-verbal and you've never had a real back and forth verbal conversation with us), then everything changes and blossoms like a garden in springtime.

Papa showing me how to pour rootbeer.

I think this will eventually make sense but you may need to read this a couple of times. I think autistics are prone to a fierce attachment to routine. Parents know our routines like Winnie the Pooh knows where to find honey...instinctual. Other caregivers will do things a little differently than parents and that's a good thing. Therapists will tell you that routine is good for us and that establishing them will enhance our comfort. That may make sense, to give us something to rely on as our autism spins us around like a top. But each time the sameness is reinforced, the roadmap in our brain becomes a deeper crevasse. What may initially start as a chicken scratch direction, written on a napkin in pencil, gradually transforms. Next time, it's written on a piece of paper in pencil, then a piece of paper in pen. Paper becomes cardstock, then cardboard, then a myriad of other materials, each getting harder in their composition. Aluminum to wood, bamboo to stainless steel to titanium, in the end, after many days of sameness in our routines, it finally gets etched in stone. Then, my dear parents, is when a therapist says you need to work on our flexibility. Where was that advice at the beginning of our autism journey together, before the napkin turned to stone? We dug this crevasse together with all those advisors' help. As well intended as it may have been, consider this:

A band-aid temporarily stops the bleeding but does nothing to rid the body of the infection caused by the cut. It's best to take the band-aid off as fast as possible even though there may be initial screaming from its wearer. Do it! Drive a different way home from school, take a new street to therapy or music class and have a helper switch days with another one. But, please do not do this without explaining to your sweet banshee, why you are messing with their utopia! Please use age-appropriate language and keep your energy calm. You'll need to be their anchor if there's a storm. Why don't you paint a picture in your head ahead of time and choose to know with confidence, that all will be well with proper preparation. That is always helpful for us.

Life is wonderful with proper rest and relaxation. You will enjoy it if you try it. We'll all get to grow and evolve because of it.

So, I pose a question to you, "Do you prefer to be in a springtime garden or on the top rung of an unstable ladder with a height phobia?" Now refer back to my earlier statement, WE ARE MIRRORS OF YOU. I speak for all children and most of humanity everywhere, when I say, "We prefer the garden in springtime!" If you maintain your flower-like energy when we do something contrary to your wishes, either voluntary or involuntarily, we will return to our flowery state faster, if not immediately. Now this may take patience from you as you may have conditioned us to respond a certain way because of your previous response patterns. So, we'll both get to practice and learn stuff. You can't just try this a few times to see what happens. Oh no, this is an evolution of you. Just choose to know it's going to work and proceed on with your life. It's a new lifestyle.

Class 6: Meaningful Days

Creativity in crafting an exciting day for your child within the public school system is required.

What do you want to accomplish at school? Is it social skills? Life skills? Academic communication? That's important to decide because you're more than likely, not going to get all of them. From what I've gathered and experienced, it's more about hanging out and being told what to do than anything else, unless you are creative.

As a parent, you really need to take an active role in your child's education and in the crafting of the IEP. That's the only way you can begin to get what you want. I just had an idea, maybe I'll pull out my last one and rewrite it for you. Wouldn't that be funny! It would be a blatant comparison of the current way we evaluate autistics, their intelligence and capabilities versus what really is.

Oh no, we'll have to go to the depths of our garage to find the binder in which these precious nuggets of misinformation are stored. If you never hear from me again, I got swallowed up by the stuff that Dad says we don't need, but that Mom has some emotional attachment to for some cute reason. (Don't worry, Mom said, "No" to this idea. I'm fine.)

Class 7: Education

Most parents will learn so much about themselves as they learn to get creative with this one. I can only talk firsthand about my personal schooling. Did you pay attention to my word choice? I'd call it an experience in which I learned a lot, but certainly not an academic education. Please beware, there are very few options for our placement in our current public school system. Special Ed classroom or general education class, with an aide or without an aide, a 1:1 aide or a shared one, inclusion or not and if so, for how long? Creativity is required in many areas as you go through the joyous process of an IEP.

Creativity in handling yourself like a sane human being during the meetings is also required. Your inner banshee tends to escape out of you more often during IEP's than any other type of meeting.

I've heard the same thing a million different times from different parents. Mom would come home from these meetings a totally different person in those early years. Dad tended to be more businesslike and logical. Mom would let her emotions get the best of her back then (she was just a beginner in my class). Her energy was often too crazy and electrifying for me after IEP's.

She was still under the impression that she could change the face of special education by herself in one meeting. It was hard for her to hear that they wanted to add a diagnosis of mental retardation to my record (yes, that term was used in 2007-2008), when she just knew it wasn't true. She believed in me so much and so did Dad, but I couldn't prove what I knew. It drove Mom crazy that others couldn't see it. She eventually got over caring what others thought but it took lots of creativity and work on herself.

Want to add some excitement to your typical classroom? Beg to have one of us join your class. Want to expand your teaching skills? Beg to have one of us join your class. Want to learn to see things from a new perspective or to stretch, expand your creativity? Beg to have one of us in your class. Oh, do you believe you are a patient person? Beg to have one of us in your class! Okay, how many of you teachers are going to run to the special education teacher and beg for inclusion, just because now you are so inspired and are in a mood to grow? I love you already and want to be friends.

Mom, Melissa and I were preparing a message we would deliver in front of a group of middle school teachers the other day. The topic they wanted us to talk on was, "How to include autistic students in the mainstream classroom," and a general overview of autism. We came across many published lists of helpful tips about inclusion. I commented on each one, as to whether I agreed or not. There were some good ideas but there were a few to which I needed to add my two cents, from someone who is actually autistic. Here are some good ones:

Advice: Help teach social rules and social behaviors, like how to approach people and taking turns.

> **My Thoughts:** Yes, because we may enjoy someone's energy and want to get closer to them sometimes.

Advice: Talk directly with as few words as possible when wanting to direct a task. "Go get your blue book from the shelf and bring it to the table."

> **My Thoughts:** True.

Advice: Do very specific tasks in order.

> **My Thoughts:** Clarity is good, but not too many baby questions.

Advice: Give two or three choices. Too many choices can cause confusion.

> **My Thoughts:** It helps to narrow the choices in most cases.

Advice: If you get no response to something you requested. Ask them to repeat it back to you to ensure they understand.

My Thoughts: Well, I don't like that one as much. Just because some of us can repeat what we've just heard, it has no bearing on our understanding. Conversely and perhaps more importantly, just because we have a blank stare or can't repeat what you said, that doesn't mean we don't understand. Remember, we have different skills than you do and language does not correspond with understanding. That's the biggest incorrect assumption that society and psychology have made about autistics! We must evolve past this not only as a society, but as fellow inhabitants of this Earth and human beings.

Advice: Idioms such as, "caught red-handed, keep your chin up, zip the lips" can really confuse autistics, so do not use them.

My Thoughts: I think most of us have heard these common idioms all our lives and understand what they mean. Just explain what they are, we understand. Society uses these, so why not educate us to these idioms? It actually could be a fun part of our education and a clever teacher could get a lot of mileage out of a lesson plan using idioms, if they can think outside the box.

Advice: Be literal in what you say. Sarcasm can be confusing to an autistic and they may take it literally.

Insight: I love sarcasm, personally, but can see that if a person has not been exposed to it, that it could be misconstrued.

Advice: Be direct in your questions and give choices rather than open ended ones, such as "what would you like to do?"

My Thoughts: I think that's true for all of us, autistic or not, especially when we're kids.

Advice: Repeat instructions and checking understanding. Using short sentences to ensure clarity of instructions.

My Thoughts: Depends which type of learner they are and which learning channel (auditory, visual, tactile, kinesthetic) is open at a particular time.

Advice: Be clear about completing something and what the goal is. Showing a picture of the end result can help.

My Thoughts: I like the second part but the first part is a little crazy. If there's a time limit on something, give us the appropriate warnings. Don't just end something abruptly. Give us time to anticipate closure and plan for it. Might help to give alternative ways of coping, too. For ex: If lunch time is ending, you could say, "You can wrap it up for later if you can't finish it."

Advice: Try to gently warn or prepare for changes in the schedule or environment.

My Thoughts: Yes, but don't you guys say it with fear in your hearts of an impending, potential meltdown from us. Have confidence that it is no big deal and that we can choose to see it that way.

Advice: Always address the child or student directly by stating their name and looking at them.

My Thoughts: Get the student's attention first, then we'll understand even if we don't hold eye contact. "OK everyone, Matteo, here's what's next."

Advice: Be informed that any change of behavior can reflect anxiety or fear in the autistic child or student.

My Thoughts: Of course, that's true but remember that all "behavior," as you call it, is actually communication. It can mean a myriad of things, including a tick of some sort or our bodies doing "their own thing," without receiving instruction from our brain.

Advice: Know that some seemingly rude or angry behavior by the child is not necessarily personal or targeted at you on purpose.

My Thoughts: It's not necessarily delivered as rude or aggressive but is interpreted as such, by most. It all depends on the judgmental mood of the recipient. Anger is an adjective commonly associated with an action of our bodies. Did you know that often times we don't have control of our bodies? We're innocent bystanders watching our bodies do something on its own, without instruction from our brains. Please avoid assigning an assumptive emotion to our bodily actions. It is rarely true, at least in my experience and that of many of my esteemed colleagues on the Spectrum. Other times we'll be reacting to a self-frustration because our bodies have a mind of their own as they do an action, while our intelligence knows better and didn't give the instruction to the body.

Advice: *Take away or minimize overstimulation or distracting things where individual work takes place. Detailed or overly colorful interiors can be distracting and difficult to cope with.*

My Thoughts: Very true. However, we can block out distractions and concentrate if the subject is exciting to our intellect.

Advice: *Always try to teach or look for ways to connect to the student's personal interests.*

My Thoughts: That's always good but keep in mind that if we are not exposed to a variety of subjects, how can we ever expand our knowledge and thus, our interests? Thomas the Train is part of my past that is easily accessed vocally, but that doesn't mean that as a thirteen-year-old boy, all I want to talk about or learn about is trains. Give me an age-appropriate education, please. Teach me the engineering and physics concepts used by trains. That's a big thing in the education of autistics. The assumption of intelligence isn't there because we can't always show you what we know. Teach us anyway, just move on and know that we know.

95

Advice: Try to incorporate computing and word processing programs into their learning.

My Thoughts: That's good for some but please never eliminate the human component. We need the human interaction and positive energy. Belief in us and our trapped intelligence is imperative, *please.*

Advice: Teach age appropriate games.

My Thoughts: Including us in a practice game is how we'll learn how to play it. Explain the rules, assume we cognitively understand them, then show us, then let us imitate you in a non-stressful environment. That's how we'll learn to play these games which are so important to our potential, new, non-autistic friends.

Advice: It is good to include peers in the free times at school or in programs. To provide support and prevent bullying.

My Thoughts: Absolutely! Instigate a peer-buddy program with neuro-typical peer buddies.

Advice: You can award good effort with allowing some obsessive behavior.

My Thoughts: OMG! Do people still believe that repetitive behavior is something that we control? If you still judge a repetitive behavior as bad and insist on stopping it, we'll just find another one to replace it when we need it. It's not something that can be imposed upon us at a time that is convenient for you. We do repetitive actions (not "behaviors") to comfort our neurological systems when we need it. Unfortunately, our needs don't always coordinate with your teaching schedule. We're sorry and don't mean to disrupt, but most people exhibit repetitive actions but ours seem to bother people more. True, flapping of hands is a bigger action than biting fingernails or twirling hair on a finger or even tapping a heel under a desk, but why don't those neuro-typicals have to stop their actions?

I have a unique opportunity to go to school as a guest student in Minnesota when we go to visit friends and family there. It's really a very special thing for me to do. I got to speak to one hundred of my peers about what it's like to be autistic and then spend the day with them in classes. My mom's college roommate, Anne, made this happen for me on a number of occasions as she's an awesome and very special 6th grade teacher. In fact, Anne and her teaching partners, plus the gym, band, choir and art teachers, the principal and the Superintendent are all gifts to the education system. That is reflected in the energy and positive vibe I feel in their school and classes.

I know what made it so successful for me was the preparation that happened before I arrived the first time. Anne gets an A+ if I was to hand out grades for autism cheerleader and Team Teo advocate. I know Anne has relayed our journey with her fellow teachers and even some of it with her students. Kind of special to have had a golden path already laid for me. All I had to do was walk on it. The kids were excited for my first talk because they were told in advance how special and unique it would be. The scene was set with positivity and anticipation. How could I lose with this attitude already in place in the teachers, kids, principal and superintendent? That's just the point. I could only succeed in my mission! The knowing was there that the kids would learn things and lives would be affected. Anne didn't stay awake the night before I was to speak, wondering if I would freeze up or embarrass her in some way.

She knew everything would be great and it would unfold the way it was supposed to. I just love that about her. She is a perfect example of the type of teacher that gives us confidence in ourselves to succeed and builds our self-esteem. Confidence in our trapped intelligence which longs to be expressed, creativity in how to include us in a typical classroom and bond with our peers and an open mind and heart to provide a simulating education to every student who comes through their door. That's our dream teacher. Take "our Anne" to the cloning machine, quickly!

Let's just keep in mind that if one's heart is open, life enhancing, creativity, will flow into it.

CHAPTER FOURTEEN

God Is The Coolest

Cool has many meanings. Let's say the sun is out on a winter day in northern California. It looks warm from inside the house but when I step outside into the fifty degree weather, it feels cool, not like at my G'ma and Papa's house in Minnesota this Christmas. That's cold! "Cool" is warmer than cold, but colder than hot. I guess you could call it a little of both.

Friends of mine act funny sometimes and make me laugh. I think they're "cool." A really friendly school is in Minnesota and I think it's "cool." Snoopy struts around on Charlie Brown shows and does whatever he wants and they call him "Joe Cool."

So, is "cool" a measure of temperature or an adjective? Just imagine if it was beholding a new meaning. Understand that many kids judge people as either "cool" or "not cool." I think adults do, too, but you can turn inward a moment and see for yourself better than I can. Seeing prevalence of this term in our society, I think I'll jump on the bandwagon and use it to describe my entire reason for existence, God's love, or plainly, God. And why wouldn't I? God encompasses all that I know to be good in this life and that's the "coolest" to me! Insert "Love Energy" for God if you want to see it that way. Conceptually, it still works as it's really the same.

God has always been there for me, that's cool. God has comforted me during the loneliest and scariest parts of my autism, also cool. God keeps his promises...important and cool. Gift giving is his favorite thing, that's way cool. Anyone that would send me Christ for a best friend definitely knows the true meaning of "cool." I'd like to include a message I wrote for my church last April 2016, for Autism Awareness Month. Mom has been speaking at church each April for the past five years about how God has affected her life with my autism. Well, last April, because of *SOMA RPM*, I shared my story. This is what I shared. I hope you enjoy it...

Autism as a spiritual way of life.

I am Matteo Musso and I am autistic. Can you believe that I chose to be autistic? Well, when I was about two years old, I lost my ability to talk, to look at you and became sensitive to just about everything. Some of you remember this. I certainly do. God asked me if I'd be willing to help autistics in this world. What was I going to say? "No?" I actually was honored and said yes. I had no idea what was in store for me. I suppose I should have found a way to ask Mom and Dad's permission, as this is quite a major decision, but I couldn't at 15 months old. I figured that Christ had them covered anyway. Then came the isolation, loneliness, weird reactions to favorite foods, scary spinning in my head, loud constant noises no one else seemed to hear and constant judgment from others who seemed to think I screamed just to bug people or to get what I wanted. And worst of all, the sadness of Mom and Dad. "Hey God", I'd say in silence. "What's up with this? I offered to help but you didn't tell me the details." Well, it was too late to back out. Besides, I promised and committed to do this. So, after life settled into a rhythm, I succumbed to being autistic.

The worst part is that people don't understand autistics at all. Doctors, teachers, psychologists, parents (no offense intended to anyone); no one gets us because they've never been autistic. Just imagine having millions of ideas and information to share but no one spoke your language. Then you were labeled mentally retarded because you didn't speak their language. Then you were put in a classroom to learn to tie shoes, play mind-numbing games and obey strict rules that made no sense. "Help!" I cried to my friend, Christ. "This can't be my life purpose! I am your messenger, your servant, your friend walking here on Earth."

Mom's eyes were opened to *RPM* and that was my miracle one year ago.

I propose to you that autism is not a "disorder" of any type, but rather a spiritual way of living. How do you medically study a spiritual existence? Yes, we have challenges that can be helped by different therapies but I'll tell you something. Since I talked to God about my challenges, he's changed my life and that of others around me. I asked for a friend I could talk to in my silence, and he gave me Christ. Christ is my buddy and constant friend. I highly suggest you carve out some time for silence each day because that's when Christ really becomes your best buddy. Take it from a silence professional it works! He loves attention from us. Not in an arrogant human way, but because he has so much to teach us about loving each other here on Earth. Decide to make this a priority and your life will be changed forever.

I Am Not Silent

I am not silent, be heard my soul,

With faith project your loving goal.

Say what you will through my silent voice,

Your lessons learned by them through choice.

You are my friend, my love, my hope,

Through you we can with all things cope.

Yours in Silence,

Matteo Musso

I have a lot more to say on this subject and that will actually be an entire book on it's own! However, I would encourage you to turn to spirituality of some sort if you interact with autistics or not. If you are teaching us, raising us or interacting with autistics in some way, spirituality will raise the effectiveness of our time together. Please notice that I didn't use the word, "religious." That was on purpose. Ego can play too big a part in organized religions sometimes, so I prefer to encourage individual relationships with God, free from judgments and the human ego. Then we can gather and share ideas and experiences we've had on our walk and spiritual journey with God. That may be at churches or at a friend's house. Don't get me wrong, there are many wonderful churches and I love mine, but there are judgments galore in some, too.

We autistics aren't even welcome in some of them. Oddly enough, some of the most severe judgments come from people attending church who see us as merely disruptions or who judge our parents for their inability to "keep us under control" during the service. Isn't that an odd contradiction, a "house of God" with so many negative judgments floating around? We've almost come to expect it in the store or in public places, but you'd think that a "House of God" would be a sanctuary, of sorts. God invites all people to gather to raise his love energy in the world but we often experience impatience and judgment there, instead. Not from God, but from people who attend to get their "weekly dose" of spiritual lessons. I think that if more people listened to what God is teaching them every day, there would be less pressure put on the actual church service itself and a different energy would exist and be created for the world.

God is the coolest type of teacher because He isn't just a boring lecturer (no offense to any of you teachers out there). No, quite the contrary. He's the hands-on, "let's experience the lesson so you'll actually remember it and use it in your life," type of teacher. If we take classes from this cool professor and learn the way He intends us to learn, then gathering at church becomes a "God energy party," where all are welcome, no matter how many classes have been taken or what grades we've earned.

I think God likes being thought of as being "cool." Many are taught to fear him and act a certain way in life because of it. My experience with God is that He is nothing but love. Energy of His love surrounds us always, even in our darkest times. Autism provides many of those times but I look back on them now as practice, homework of sorts, from classes that teach us to call on Him for help and comfort. Classes that teach patience and self-respect and classes designed to remind us of the gifts He's given us, even when they seem to be lost sometimes in fear and hopelessness.

Is God powerful, capable of anything, in charge of the universe? Of course, but when He is also only full of love while being all those things, that's when He entered the realm of being "cool." This society loves "cool" things, and for this kid, "God is the Coolest!"

CHAPTER FIFTEEN

Would I Choose It Again?

Having choices is a luxury of the human condition but it also comes with responsibility. Are you ready for this? People do choose their paths in some respects, and in others, they only choose their reactions to circumstances. There, I said it. I began saying in the first chapter of this book, that I chose this condition by agreeing to help God with the special group of people labeled autistic. I also am a pleaser of sorts so I didn't really understand what it would be like, exactly, to be autistic. Can you imagine that during some of my teaching sessions (some call them meltdowns or tantrums), I questioned the wisdom of my decision? I am reminded of my humanness and teach myself patience with the help of my angels and God. It's hard sometimes, especially in the midst of zealous confusion.

Do you know what makes autistics confused? Oh, just a few things like an obsession with the spoken word, for example. Speech, oh speech, why dost thou forsaken me? Blah, blah, blah! Did you ever watch Charlie Brown? The teacher communicates with sounds alone, yet all the kids seem to perfectly understand her or him. What's up with that? Are they all autistic, aliens, or just super cool and powerful? Words are really confusing if you think about it. And not just for autistics. This I know, from my sociological observations.

First of all, how many words, in the English language, at least, sound the same when spoken, look different in their spelling and most significantly, mean completely different things? No and know, time and thyme, knot and not, and Mom's favorite, sail and sale! There are many more but alas, no time (not thyme) to list them all here. That's just a basic confusion about grammar. Let's just call it "Auditory Grammatical Confusion, AGC." Next, we have what I'll call "Pleaser People Disorder, PPD." PPD is diagnosed (by yours truly), when one says words that come from the manufacturing center in the brain, not directly from ones heart, as their truth. How backwards is that? We autistics just tell it like it is until we get in trouble or get "programmed" to answer with just one socially appropriate response.

Ever wonder why some of us non-verbal (pre-verbal really, when you figure out that it's possible for each of us to talk someday) autistics just start laughing during your conversations? We hear you do this all the time with each other. After awhile, when we figure out what a curious world we've entered, we've just gotta laugh! We can feel and know how you truly feel. I guess you could call it our sixth or seventh sense, of sorts.

Anyway, back to it. Often, those who suffer with PPD find themselves saying the opposite of what they really feel, in an effort to impose an emotion onto someone else, which they feel would be appropriate in a situation. PP's (people pleasers), have some control issues, however well-intended the words may be. The funniest example of late, has been to watch my G'ma Mary try to get people, usually her guests, to sit in certain places. They'd be fine in one chair, but she feels they'd be more comfy in another. I think she may have been deprived of playing musical chairs in her youth. Dad and I are so happy that it appears Mom has inherited this gene, the "I know where you'll feel most comfortable because that's where I'd feel so," gene (the IKWYFMCBTWIFS gene, for short). Honestly!

Kids are more honest until they're taught not

to be, until they're labeled "rude, selfish or obnoxious." I'm not saying that we should just comment on everything we see, because sometimes people's emotional management skills aren't real refined. But then again, if we stopped judging each other based on our own life experiences, we wouldn't have so much to worry about. Poof! People's personalities are no longer weird, they just are. Body types aren't good or bad, they just are. People's facial features are no longer attractive or unattractive, they're merely a means to communicate emotions without words. Skin has no color and speech accents have no hidden secrets.

Would I choose it again? The answer is, "*Yes.*"

CHAPTER SIXTEEN

Bye For Now and Thanks For Reading

I now think its time to stop bleeding so much information and just speak from my heart. Heart comprises us, it's not only an organ. With that in mind, I hope the information I've shared in this book will touch your heart in many ways. I hope you'll just consider what it means to turn hope into knowing. Once you know in your heart that your autistic buddy is perfectly intelligent and present behind his veil of autism, a new world can open up to you and your family. You may even choose a different approach to things you do with and for him. For your 13-year-old autistic teenager, books will change from those comfort, picture, stimming books that you're so sure he still loves to read, to age-appropriate chapter books like Harry Potter. Thanks Mom and Dad, as much as I love Llama Llama Red Pajama, I'm ready to move on.

I hope from my heart to yours, that you'll choose to provide your child with an age-appropriate education with stimulating opportunities for exposure to all sorts of cool information and subjects, even if he or she can't communicate back what they know to you. Just feed them the information with respect for the knowing and comprehension that they have.

I hope that you will continue forever, your search for new ways to bond and communicate with your autistic friend. Talking to them in age-appropriate, respectful vocal tones about deep, meaningful subjects, even though the conversation may be one-sided. Sharing heart-felt information is the best way to deepen any friendship and human bond. We are no different.

I hope, from my heart to yours, that you find inner peace on your journey, for that is the ultimate lesson of this life. It's the summit of experiencing love and humanness. If we attain inner peace throughout life's challenges, then climbing Mt. Everest becomes a stroll in the park on a new spring day.

How to do that is different for everyone but there is a common thread among us all. None of us is meant to find it alone. Family and friends are God's gifts to us. Let them help. Know that a power greater than any human, whose love for us surpasses our understanding, supports us on our quest. As I said before, give this any name you'd like that works in your belief system and comforts you. I choose God, but you may choose energy or something else, it just doesn't matter. What's in a name? Just know that there's always help available if you want it.

I hope, from my heart to yours, that you notice the people that appear in your life. I think it's so fun how they show up at the exact time we really need them. Let them in, listen to new ideas and say thank you. Then take what you want and disregard the rest. That's what we do and it really works well.

I leave you with a thought or lyric poem:

Thank you, new friends who have opened these pages as a symbol of opening yourself to a new idea or two.

Reality is so beautiful, when kindness and acceptance is the foundation on which our village is built. Love and curiosity blend in a crockpot left to simmer on low. Hours upon hours pass, becoming months, then years. All the while, the flavors blending lusciously.

Until the surprising entrée is complete. It was not rushed or cooked too fast, for that makes it tough.

Instead it simmered, taking all the time given and all the time needed, to develop into a gourmet meal. Tender and savory, the perfect flavor of love, sautéed with patience, acceptance, joy, curiosity, respect, wonder and divine inspiration. A meal for the most gracious and cherished of humankind.

Welcome to the table my new friends...
dinner is served.

Love, Teo

P.S. I'd love to share some special things with you. Just turn the page and keep on reading!

CHAPTER SEVENTEEN

My Scrapbook

Some of my favorite thoughts, poems,
and life experiences.

Bellowing Waters
By Matteo Musso, February 9, 2016
·

Bellowed the waterfall to the stream,
Understand that we are one and the same.
Different forms we take
But of the same energy made.
Now you flow as gently as a newborn baby sleeps,
Down to the valley to nourish life itself.
Will you have the power to kiss all those in need?
I am here for you in strength and plenty
If you will only call on me for help.
I am the source of your abundance,
And the way to end the thirst of the world.

I Bellow Still

By Matteo Musso, January 29, 2017
Written at the same waterfall one year later.

I am still here.
I've waited for your return to this place.
This place that remains constant and nourishing to
those who seek it's nourishment and gifts.
Welcome back to the beginning,
A place which promises the renewal of spirit
And a life kissed by mother nature.
I've called you before today and waited for
your reply.
Listen, just listen
For my sounds to rush through your heart and soul,
Bringing refreshment and cleansing.
Last year at this time I had more struggles,
For natures raindrops were limited.
I prayed and knew the heavens would open.
Now more powerful songs are composed
And the Messages sing a louder tune.
I Bellow from atop my waterfall which has
learned throughout the ages,
Love trickles down and flows to those willing
to receive it in its most simple and purest form.
Welcome, all of you, to the reception of love.
Whether you hiked through treacherous waters,
Crossed back-and-forth over my flowing stream,
Carefully climbed my mountain one step at a time
to see my glorious beginning or have walked my path
for many days and now wait for me
to answer your call to come to you,
It matters not.
I am here. Always.

I Hear You Whispering Gently
By The Stream

By Matteo Musso, January 29 , 2017

Let life flow, you say.
You need not worry about the direction,
speed or duration of the journey you are on.
It is as natural as this stream,
That I am your captain.
I steer and direct your path,
So which decisions do you ponder?
You whisper to me.
I am the most trusted captain
And the flow is easy,
With trust and knowing.

My buddy, Nikolay.

Nikolay: Sorry I am so annoying.
(Trying to grab Teo's plate while he's eating lunch.)

Matteo: No! Are you serious?

Nikolay: Yeah. Maybe I'm being dramatic?

Matteo: I think so. Maybe tell me why you think that.

Nikolay: I am thinking because I know that's what other people think.

Matteo: I am sure I know that feeling, but I am telling you that you are never annoying.
Nikolay: Hey, thanks. Every now and then I need

to be reminded of that. What's your secret to a happy soul?

Matteo: My secret is true love and to be patient. Grounding yourself in that true love.

Nikolay: Wow, are you a genius? That's very special. I am lucky to know you.

Matteo: Thanks Friend. I am even more lucky to know you. On the topic of souls, how is yours?

Nikolay: My soul is fussy. Like a new born baby. It's scared and blissfully happy.

Sugar Poem
By Matteo Musso

I had a lesson about how plants make their food and photosynthesis. They use CO_2 and H to make sugars. I had to write a poem about my favorite food.

S Sugar is so sweet.

U Utter the word and I drool.

G Gonna eat some candy.

A And if you give me sugar

R Really, I will die!

Music

I have studied the spiritual lives of major composers. Mom and I like to listen to their music and discuss it. I close my eyes and listen, first, coming up with adjectives to describe the piece, then I write something about what I hear.

Die Forelle

Franz Schubert

(As described by Matteo Musso)

Adjectives:
Wanting freedom, tricky notes, lopsided music.

The voice teases me with movements
up and down,
Yo-yo like in distance, yet jolly like a clown.
My interest is peaked, the sounds are so sweet,
I give my attention to notes, and I'll keep
My mind and my heart on high alert
So I'll hear you and feel you, the learnings convert
From mere notes and sounds,
they become love from you,
To share with each other and myself, too.

Music For The Royal Fireworks

George Frederick Handel

(As described by Matteo Musso)

Adjectives: Majestic, grand, declarative,
having respect.

There he stood in all his glory
The one who loved so pure.
His purple light in all it's splendor
And my soul redeemed, for sure.

Reverently, I listen
As each note makes it's point.
The sounds fill my body
As no other sound could.

Hallowed by thy name
Let this world know,
Your love reigns still
I love you so.

Part II • Music For The Royal Fireworks

George Frederick Handel

(As described by Matteo Musso)

Part II gets more lively.

Adjectives: Rugged, happily excited, persistently
rowdy, fantasy at it's finest.

I see them running free amongst the redwoods,
The air so crisp and filled with the playful,
happy endurance of the human race.
They call for us to run with them in harmony
and peace.
They are the souls of those we love,
Who speak to us from heaven through
mother nature's beauty.
Let us all join together in the celebration of life.
For it is truly a gift from god, as is the life
everlasting.

My fellow scouts, George and Chris,
on March 27, 2017

This is me, receiving my *Public Speaking* merit badge at the Boy Scout Court of Honor. Two years ago I could never have dreamed this, a kid who has trouble talking is awarded for being a public speaker. I love just being one of the guys.

Me and Dad happy on the boat!

After Whale Watching In Maui

By Matteo Musso • February, 2017

I wrote about my experience
on the catamaran.

So I sat there, consumed by my chicken wings, perfectly happy and at peace on the boat. Then all the sudden it happened. Whales emerged from the ocean like mountains emerge from the sea. The difference is one emerged in an instant, and the other over millions of years. Which is more magnificent?

Let's ponder...

Well mother, well baby,
Thank you for your bravery.
Traveling far, under the sea,
What a gift you came to me.

Mounting, mountain, where is your mom?
I long to climb you, big and strong.
You must be brave to stand alone,
Here I come, you feel like home.

How to compare these two dumbfound
The naturalist in each of us, I've found.
Both are alive and still evolving,
Man's souls still crave that which they're solving.

Whales played and breathed and slapped
and breached,
The site was what God's always preached.
Love, protect, accept and know
My love rains down to you below.

May you enjoy the whales from me
And learn from them about being free.
There is a price being free does have,
Love, trust and knowing, must forecast.

So what I mean by that, we know,
Our lives on earth are so we'll grow.
Just like the whales breech to the sky,
My love reaches you and will til night.

So if you breach even as man
Let my love enter, it truly can.
Let nature teach what you must know
Let love encompass you, then grow.

Surfing in Maui with my instructor Zak.

Dream Surfing
By Matteo Musso • February, 2017

Can you come and play my friend?
Can I tempt you to live an inner dream?
Step off the shore and come to me.
I will protect your body while thrilling your soul.
Do I frighten you my friend?
My sounds can be mighty and my force can
get fierce,
But that is not today, my friend.
Today I am rolling
and each time I fold, I give you a gift.
Do you want to open me and truly feel what I am?
God wrapped me this morning for you, my friend.
Energy builds up slowly then surprises your senses
with the ride of your life.
Can you come and play my friend?
Enter the water.
Trust. Breathe. Wait.
I will come to you.

Yes, that's me and I'm up!

After surfing...

May I say, surfing in the ocean of Hawaii is magical. It was like opening yourself up to God and letting his grace into your soul and heart. Can't acquire it without experiencing it first. To watch surfers crevasse these majestic waves of nature is inspiring and awesome. To ride a wave your self, with a confident friend like Zak, is akin to doing that which you never dreamed could happen to you. Dream surfing came true for me today and my heart sings.

Brainiac Waits

By Matteo Musso • October 24, 2016

Do you get mad when nobody is listening?

Do you have faith that the body is glistening?

Do you have a way to show your smarts?

Must you wait for their learning to start?

Dad just finished making the best chili ever!
I just finished my third bowl.

On a Chili Night
Matteo Musso • January 4, 2017

There he stood in the kitchen, Dad in his glory.
He tosses and blends, like a culinary chef's story.

What shall I add next? His brain asks with a flurry.
If it's beans, meat and sauce, it becomes chili in a hurry.

Resigned to the pot, the ingredients simmer.
Soon they will become, my Wednesday night dinner.

(Dad: How did he know it was Wednesday? Who told him?
Me: It logically arrives after Tuesday.)

Go down my throat, after I chew you.
Or I am afraid, that I'll have to sue you.

Reluctant it flowed, right to my tummy.
I'm glad that it did, cuz it was so nummy!

My hat's off to Dad, who created this grub.
Remember this recipe, we'll start a chili club!

Thanks for the loving dinner, Dad.

Love, Teo

My two favorite people in the whole world!

And you wonder why?

I dared Mom to take me zip lining. I can't believe we actually did it!

Mom is a good sharer.

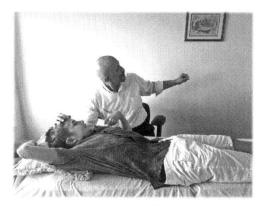

The Truth About Silence

Matteo Musso • March 8, 2016
Matteo wrote this poem from 2:45-3:00 pm on this day after
his silent *Shafaw* healing session with Master Donadoost.

The truth talks, the message sings
You hear it only in solitude.
A message comes, you feel it now
Amidst life's challenges, it thrills the soul.
Hark, says the author of the silent message
I'm glad the time with you alone has come.
Good peace I give you while you are listening.
Breathe deeply and let me flood your body with love.
How busy you are with thoughts yet untrue
That my messages of comfort cannot break through.
Christ has a voice louder than all,
Want to hear it? Just give Him a call.
The minutes and airtime are free to you
The love and healing energy is, too.
What's in store for you, my friend
Is comfort and peace that does not end.
Be still my soul, He is the Lord.
To Him I dedicate this every word.

Master Donadoost likes to dress like me.

Universal Learning

Matteo Musso • September 9, 2016

Today, I was inundated with information about our galaxy, the universe and planets. It just so happened that all of my teachers are focused on these same things. Then, in a teaching session tonight with Master Donadoost, he spoke of "time" and how we actually have control over it. Master asked, "Why do fun times seem to go by so fast and the boring or negative times go so slow? Shouldn't we be choosing the opposite?" I combined all the lessons of today into this story...

Universe Created

Matteo Musso • September 9, 2016

A whirling mass of worldly particles is twirling
round and round.

Universes collide at colossal speed, we go along
for the ride.

Hang on real tight the driver shouts,

There's going to be a crash!

Keep hands and feet in at all times

'Cuz a BANG will cause a flash!

Kind of serious, don't you think?

To move things oh so fast?

You might end up with more types of life

Than ever, in the past.

Haha, you're right! God said to them

I am the great Creator.

More types of life I want right now

So I'll say good-bye till later.

And later came in an instant

Or in a million years,

God said, "We're here – live happily!

You'll have both smiles and tears."

Lots of time was made and spent

But they have not realized

That the time they have is not short or long

But determined by their lives.

Happy times just cruise on by

And tough times tend to linger.

Why do they choose that? Wonders he

It's quite an odd hum-dinger.

You can stretch the happy and shorten the yuck

It's just as easy to see

Through eyes of love God's love abounds

And happier you will be.

So now you know, secrets have been shared

With info, what will you choose?

Extend the joy and stretch the love?

What have we got to lose?

The black hole then became littered with sadness, hate,
misery and jealousy...all that humans decided to discard.
And all was well in the universe once more.

Sara, one of my *RPM* teachers, taught me about Mars and wanted me to give a weather report from there...

> *Good morning America. Matteo Musso maybe live, reporting from mars. Can't breath. I get why only dust prevails. There is not much time. I am going to call. Backing out of this report. Have a good morning. Teo out.*

And my moon report:

> *This is Matteo Musso reporting live from the moon. Nothing is happening. Can't breathe. I am losing consciousness. Now back to you in the studio.*

My Letter to San Francisco Symphony conductor

January, 25, 2017

Dear Mr. Reif,

I am Matteo Musso, a 13-year-old guy with autism. I attended the Concert for Kids today with my mom, my friend Nickolay, and his mom. Until about 12 years ago I was silent, but I can now express myself spelling one letter at a time on a simple alphabet stencil. Mom takes dictation and has learned this amazing approach to communicate with me. I have so much locked up inside and it likes to ooze out best through poetry. I thought I'd write a poem to you and the musicians about my experience today at the concert.

...To be continued, read on.

Soul Bathing

Thankful notes released from the pages of music,
found each other and collaborated in my ears.
The sounds that were created kissed my soul.
Remember the first breath of spring as the flowers
opened up their faces and smiled at the sun?
Or a walk in the redwoods after a springtime rain
when the air is crisp and the oxygen so pure?

Your music today accosted my senses and radiated
joy throughout my being. Gone are the days of my
oversensitive sensory system and my soul rejoices.
Notes are allowed to enter me and fill my spirit once
again.

Happiness, joy, thrill, dance, smile, relax, absorb and
nourish...these are words of the music you gave to
me today.

Thank you for speech that transcends human barriers
and penetrates the life of this kid. Your talent shared
today was a peaceful bath for my soul.

My definition of music:

Music is nourishment for our souls with different
vibrational speeds and frequencies intersecting to
affect us emotionally. Different ones and combina-
tions affect us differently and depend on our own
simple caring each day. It also depends on our
openness to let it affect us.

Love, Matteo

Mom, me, G'ma and Papa excited for the concert to begin.

Hi Mr. Reif,

I just received your letter and wanted to thank you for taking time to write it to me. I think you express yourself very well with words, too!

When I listen to music I get filled with such emotion and now I have a way to get it out of me. It comes out through the poetry. Since you seem to enjoy poetry, I thought I'd send you some of my "musical poetry." (I think I may have invented a new poetic form...I'm not sure.) I hope you like it as you listen to the music in your head. I like to write poetry from many perspectives, all rolled into one. One can read each poem three times, or maybe more. Read them from a music theory perspective, a spiritual perspective and from that of a silent autistic's perspective. I'd love to get your feedback.

Regarding your generous offer to attend the Youth Symphony concert, mom is going to try to work that out so we can come. I really want to! And I'd love to meet and chat with you sometime! I'm sure you're busy on concert days so we can get together any time. I am homeschooled, so very flexible. If Mom does work it out to come to the concert, is there any way I could bring my grandma and grandpa? They're visiting from Minnesota and would love to attend. Dad may want to come, too. We'd be happy to purchase their tickets but do not know if the concert is sold out. What do you think?

Have a happy day, my new friend.

Love,
Matteo

I got invited to meet and speak with Christian Reif
after the concert. He's an amazing conductor
and all-around cool guy!

I wrote this afterwards...

CLAP!
By Matteo Musso • March, 5, 2017

One might liken today at the symphony to a novel filled with romance, dancing and peace, lively chatter and erupting emotions. Notice the erupting emotions happened first.

The Barber (Second Essay for Orchestra) was depicting our soul's decision to live, I mean, really live! Should it remain in a state of stagnancy, or should it take a chance on living life to it's fullest?

Our soul holds an inner debate, being introduced to the vigorous ups and downs of being human. Contentment versus challenge, kind harmonies versus dissonance, sweet softness versus loud shocks of jagged sounds...they culminate in a smorgasbord of senses leaving our soul craving more sensations. The rest is over. It's time to truly experience our humanness.

Enter Mozart (Symphony No. 41, Jupiter), the first welcome to our hearts. "Welcome. So glad you're here," sing the concierge-like notes of the Jupiter Symphony. Reliable, comforting sounds stream toward our souls with an embrace of anticipation that drives us onward. To where shall I go? The predictable progressions comfort us in this new adventure, giving us energy while providing just enough curiosity and filling our need for growth. The notes provide safe respite as we know always, that a fulfilling resolution is on the way. Uplifted and confident, we venture onward and dare to seek the most powerful emotion of all, the one that's got the ultimate strength to transform every heart and the entire world...love.

Cheer on Dvorak (Symphony No. 8) for his depiction of love through our auditory system! Storing up note after note in an invisible vat built by God to hold infinite pounds of weightless love, Dvorak seems to get this idea. Keep adding beautiful notes of kindness and chords of good deeds, and the love multiplies. Singing melodies emit tempting lures and we are hooked! We can't help but join in the game of goodness. The sounds are just too beautiful to leave behind, so we follow the guidance of this beautiful music until our hearts are filled with immense joy and a desire to share this feeling with others on our journey. It culminates in us. Then the final exclamation is revealed.

We put our hands together, over and over, making them musical instruments of their own, in an effort to let the emotion out. We want to feel our body again after our emotional emersion, "CLAP." We want to show our thanks and gratitude to composers, musicians and conductors, "CLAP." We want to live life anew and refreshed, "CLAP." But most of all, my hands want to be percussive with thanks to God for my human experiences, especially those today, "CLAP, CLAP, CLAP!"

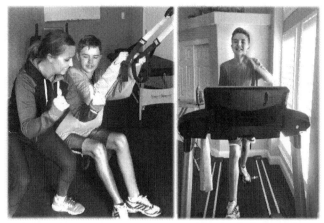

My trainer and friend, Jen Kinney
helps me "work it!"

Exercise feels so good.

Exercise Sonnet
Matteo Musso • January, 2017

I learned that a sonnet has 13 lines with 10 syllables per line.

Shall I compare thee to a singing kid?
Thy body remembers the feeling strong.
To want you is not enough, oh feeling.
Thou hast required commitment from me.
Thou hast touched my cardiac system now.
Daily shall I attend thee, Exercise.
For you bear gifts of rejuvenation.
Walking daily and Lifting heavy things.
Oh, body of mine these gifts art for thee.
Added joy thou bringst, oh my Exercise.
Really effective results shall be mine.
I willst deliver mine body for you.
Exercise exercise wherefore art thou?
Later today thou shallt mine be again.

More Love Than Hate • A 9/11 Tribute

By Matteo Musso, Age 11, September 12, 2016

I meet perceptions from videos and stories about the day we were attacked and I surmise that man alone did this. Under the guise of hate, they came to us with their misguided beliefs unveiled through horror. Lost were thousands among us that day, planting seeds of sadness throughout our nation. Young and old, race and beliefs, occupation and status, male and female, these things that often divide us were all united in non-discriminatory acts of violence. The hate did not discriminate. Hate ensures equality among its victims. Love reassured its power that day. It too, does not discriminate. Love has the unique ability to multiply exponentially. Hate must churn slowly in cauldrons by those who choose it.

We saw it happen before our eyes that day, love's growth and expansion. Humanity around our country and the world united in compassion, action, heroism, prayer, awareness and resolve. Find it today in yourself. How will you share it in a non-discriminatory way? Brainstorm for one minute in silence. Do you have a pattern in your love? Give it today to someone who is lost or outside your comfort circle. That's the exponent in our algebraic equation of life. Hate did not win on September 11, 2001. More love grew that day than ever before.

Let's honor the lives lost from this earth that day with exponents of love and compassion. Their legacy continues to make this world a strong beacon of love.

There is no cauldron big enough to destroy love that is in our hearts.

My current RPM teachers and friends.

Chatting with Sara.

Being sassy with Kim.

Learning with Soni.

Brenton is teaching me
computer programming.

My talk to psychology students • February 23, 2017

Las Positas College Psychology Club

*"As psychologists, teachers and caring people in
general, help autistics enter the world
as leaders, not followers."*

Matteo Musso

Open your mind to see other ways of existing on this planet. We have no disorder. We are a different type of spiritual being...that's all. Discover our challenges one at a time and figure out how to help us. Being comfortable on this Earth would be nice and some therapies would help.

Look for our gifts and focus on them. First of all, we will need exposure to a variety of things and an overall education, like everyone else. Teach us and assume we understand. Assume intelligence, even if we can't communicate what we know in a way you understand.

Think outside the box. The box is boring! Be creative in securing a future for us as entrepreneurs, teachers, or some other important part of society.

We lead by example. Leading by exposing you to our challenges and showing society what changes need to happen to secure a safe, healthy, happy, loving world, is our mission.

Let go of assumptions and be examples of truth to your peers, family and friends. Once you start examining your beliefs, you'll discover how many were actually "imposed" on you. Keep or change them...it's up to you.

Live and let live. Why must we all conform, lest we get labeled "off" or "weird?" Have confidence in your convictions. Do this throughout your life and attract others to your positivity toward individuality and expressive living.

Turn *believing* into *knowing* and say goodbye to stress, doubt and worry. When you KNOW all things contribute to your journey and your learnings and that they are from God/Universe (or the name you call the Higher Power) with a loving purpose, you start searching for the good in each situation. Keep in mind that sometimes it might be buried and harder to see right away.

I Wait

By Matteo Musso • September 28, 2016

My Child, how are you doing?
I have been calling you.
Do you have a minute to talk?

I know you are busy but time can stand
still for our conversation.

I hear your questions and they are so clear.
Why don't you hear my answers?

Good will can exist between you and me.
I am still your rock, come and hold on to me.

My victory awaits, it's yours for the taking.
No time is for me but for others you're making.

Remember, my child, I speak in a whisper.
Stop filling your time with all things that are
yelling.

You need the softness much more than the loud.
For without the quiet, the loud becomes noise.

In your solitude, seek me, my friend.

And I am here...waiting.

Me as a professional chef for the day at *Boudins*,
San Francisco, with their Executive Chef Misael Reyes.

Me as a professional eater.

Hot Tamale

By Matteo Musso • November 4, 2016

Hey, Hot Tamale! Why do you hurt my mouth so?
You started out so innocently as maize and meat,
Then you transformed into something hot,
not so sweet.
You want to be eaten, that's proof on my plate,
Can't eat you so fast so at the table I wait.
"Digest now!" I say, to bites inside me.
There's more to come, laugh all you want,
I'll digest you, you'll see!
Well, my plate still has more and you know
I can't throw it,
So eat you I will, or maybe I'll stow it.

Leaves Falling In The Breeze

By Matteo Musso • November 4, 2016

In the form: AAAA BBBB

Why do you fall, little leaf?
Don't give your mother grief.
Eat enough and sleep beneath
The others kindly beds bequeath.
Little Leaf began his journey
Quite excited it was his turny.
So off he flew, the breeze was surely
Taking him to find a girly.

Brandenburg Concertos

J.S. Bach

(As described by Matteo Musso)

Adjectives: Conflict with resolution,
moving parts, reinforcing,
needing attention, acrobatic.

I see a candle flickering in the breeze,
Flickering wildly within the seas.
How can it be? Is what you ask,
Nothing is too great a task.

For God is great,
And God is good.
His praise be endless,
As your reverence should.

Repeat it once again and continue on,
Other keys, other choices, life goes on.
People listen, hear the sound,
His love through Christ to you abound.

Trumpet Concerto

By Haydn

(As described by Matteo Musso)

Adjectives: Happy, tuneful,
conversational, reinforced.

Blowing sounds fly through the air,
A mostly happy tune, I hear.
They talk back and forth,
Those in number and the one alone.
Keep it coming, says the one,
Our dialogue has just begun.
I have so much to say,
That the world must hear someday.
Your voices so strong,
That together they'll hear my song.
You cannot see,
What making music together means to me.
A mighty word to the world...
We must allow each other to be,
All unique, with gifts from Thee.

Symphony # 3 " Eroica," Mvmt. I

By Beethoven

(As described by Matteo Musso)

Adjectives:
Longing to be heard, Trying hard to resolve things,
Love despite conflict.

An utter grievance shows itself requesting to be heard
Maybe not as kindly as the song of a bird.
But worth a listen, nonetheless,
And shared by most in humanness.
Can we flourish by ourselves while alone we remain?
My heart says "no" and asks us all to change.
While we can survive, it doesn't necessarily
mean we'll thrive.
Let's gather up each stray note and compose a
symphony of hope.
Some will lead and others will follow.
Some need repeating while others are singular
and take us to a new place within ourselves.
All the while making music played by a society struggling
to find its peace.
Reigning hope prevails in my heart for us.
Let perfect love enter with each breath
And the One who loves us will do the rest.

Piano Sonata in Bb Major, K.333

By Mozart

(As described by Matteo Musso)

Adjectives:
Goodness, happiness, time passing quickly,
Prickly.

Stay youthful, the old man cried,
My life today is filled with pride.
Open your eyes and you will find,
Much more to life when you are kind.
A look, a hug, a smile, a word,
These are those longing to be heard.
Look real hard at the one in the mirror,
The one you see has Him so near.
To those who have a mirror not,
You're the ones God inside has taught.
Mirror or nor, it makes no difference,
We all can change the world.
You have lips to smile, arms to hug,
Eyes to see or a voice to speak.
The most important though, has not been told,
It's not the cash but the heart of gold.

Concord Piano Sonata

By Charles Ives

(As described by Matteo Musso)

Adjectives: Intensity, challenging, talking voices.

Treat them with respect and they sing together.
Discordance prevails when respect is a forgotten jewel.
Listen to the quiet times, as there can be gentle
disagreement without discordance.
The crowds shout their angry surprises begging
to be heard among the mass of similarity.
Rescue the few who bring light into a world
casting shadows.
Talk to one another, unless the music is too loud.
In that case, we have no choice but to sing.
The world needs all of its musical notes to compose
its masterpieces.
Remember, that rests are just as important.

CHAPTER EIGHTEEN

From My Mom

As I sit here with my laptop, I wonder where in the world will I find the words to express just an ounce of my amazing life journey with my son. A message that relays, not only what my son has taught me just by being him, but also what I have chosen to learn by being his mom. I feel an inner calling to share some emotionally intimate details of my experiences raising an autistic child. I want to offer an invitation, especially to those parents of "special" children. There is a great contrast between the way I used to be and the way I am today. My life has changed dramatically because of one word, perspective. The beauty of perspective is that we all have it, it's free, and we can change it anytime.

If you have read this book so far, then you now know a good deal about my son. For my husband, Mark and me, it was a long and windy road to finally have the miracle of knowing him. For the last twelve years I have been saying in my head; "I know my son the best. He does this because of that," or "he would rather, blah blah blah." I was truly doing the very best I could to understand my son and his likes, dislikes, attitudes, desires, needs and wants – all without his use of the spoken word!

I was told over and over by professionals, that autistics (the term Teo uses, so I'll use it, too) have a hard time communicating. So, from day one of Matteo's diagnosis at age three, I got this stuck in my brain. My brain had pigeonholed communication into the tiny space of speech. I found I was not the only one who had fallen into this hole. The rest of the things my son would do would be given other names like behaviors, stims, isms and responses. Now, I finally know they are all communications. Come to find out my son is a *communication expert* and the rest of us are the ones stuck in the pigeonhole! It's really difficult to see from in that hole and it wasn't until I found the strength to climb out into the light, that I have been able to truly understand.

You may be thinking, "Yeah, easy for you to say. You can actually communicate with your son, I can't." Trust me, I get that. I had read beautiful autism stories online or in the news and it was always someone else's "success story," not mine. I was at home experiencing quite a different world.

At the beginning of our autism journey, I was given books written by parents of people with autism sharing their journeys. I'd eagerly open them, read the first chapter, but be unable to continue. The detailed emotional descriptions and life changing sorrow of their child's transformation into autism was just too much to bare. I couldn't read someone else's experience which was all too similar to my own pain. What I really wanted was someone to grab my hand, look me in the eyes and tell me that everything was going to be okay. That life was just taking a really unexpected turn  but that the journey was going to be extraordinarily good. I longed for *any* assurance that there would be light at the end of the tunnel and that I wouldn't feel this way for the rest of my life. I craved honesty about our son's potential that pointed to real hope.

Well, that is what I hope you will choose to find in this message, from one loving ent. Because guess what? Everything will be okay. This journey of parenting an autistic child can be one of the most extraordinary experiences of your life and it will be even more beautiful in ways you never imagined.

What I learned was that someone else's perception of my son's potential has nothing to do with the *reality* of his potential. I finally saw that the tunnel was full of light! I saw it when I opened my eyes. Hope? It's great! It's wonderful! I'd even say it's fabulous and it feels so good! The only downside I've found with hope is that it can change or evaporate the minute things don't go my way, in my time. Did that mean that I actually had control over my own "hope?" That it was mine when I felt good, successful, like I'm doing the right thing for my son and then it disappeared when I chose to see stagnancy and "regression," and feel stress and exhaustion?

That's when a wonderful friend of mine introduced me to the idea of knowing as a replacement for hoping. Hope is emotional and variable but once you know something, you know it. Done! The trick for me was realizing that to know whatever was happening at the current time was part of our journey and taking us to the next place. If we stop the journey out of fear or frustration, we don't get to go to the next place. My journey was having beautiful ups and crazy, stressful downs. But without all of them, I know I wouldn't be on the most surprising, joyful and enriching ride of my life with my son.

My friend Valle was with me at that first

professional meeting where the State of California refused to diagnose my son with autism. This was even after he stacked blocks and knocked them down, right in front of them, repetitively for a solid three hours in silence and isolation. I was told by one of the professional diagnosticians, "Don't worry (I felt her pat, pat, pat, my shoulder). He just needs an hour of Occupational Therapy each week and he'll be just fine." When we got out of that room, Valle said something to me that I've never forgotten: "You will find the things that will help him. You're his mom and your love for him will guide you. God chose *you* to parent Matteo for a reason." Eleven years later, just this last year, I was able to remind her of those comforting words she shared which hung with me throughout my entire journey. I thanked her again and this time, Matteo was able to thank her with his letter board. What a gift.

I add "believing" into this same category as "hoping." At certain times during this personal autism journey, I truly believed that I was so "right." My passion drove me onward to push for certain things at IEP's, fight for services from our health insurance company, etc. In addition, I believed that if I was not successful in acquiring these services for my son, his life would be severely negatively impacted...basically, *ruined*!

And it would be all my fault! I've never been so thankful for the fact that beliefs change if I want them to.

That was a huge learning experience for me and one that I hadn't really pondered before. In the past, stuff just "happened" in life and I would react to it. There was no "filter" between the stimulus and the response, that twisted everything into "happiness." The way I was reacting to things that happened in my life were much easier to blame on other people's behaviors, than on how I chose to respond to them. After lots of hard, emotional work running a *Son-Rise* Program for Matteo, my husband and I experienced a truly magnificent and powerful shift in our attitudes and approach to stimulus in our lives. We transformed into more of a team than we ever were, in our quest to help our son live life to its fullest.

Together, Mark and I were determined to help Matteo in whatever way possible, to be a strong contributor to society, help him be comfortable in this world, experience true happiness and most importantly, feel and know the love we have for him. We wanted him to know that we felt so blessed to have him as our son and that he was perfect exactly the way he was! He didn't have to change a bit to "fit in" or conform to society's limited expectations. As long as he remained safe and wasn't harming others on purpose, his actions are his business. If he needed to flap his hands in public to feel comforted, we'd say, "Flap away, my friend. We think it's so cool that you have found a way to take care of yourself because we know we cannot possibly understand the challenges that this world provides you. We love you!" And during the three years we were running Teo's *Son-Rise* program at home, we'd join him in his flapping (or whatever repetitive action he was involved in at the time), and have a ball! *Son-Rise* taught us to join him in his world and then eventually invite him to cross the bridge into ours. We stopped judging his behavior as good or bad. We thought, it just "is." Since we may not understand why he's choosing to do a particular behavior, we chose to assume that he is just taking care of himself in the best way he could.

In my son's case, at that time, it was repetitively throwing rocks over the fence in our backyard for hours at a time. We all know that throwing rocks, however small and however gently, is not really appropriate social behavior. But on top of that, I was carrying out a previous program in which I was taught to exchange unwanted behavior immediately with wanted behavior and never, never let them be idle because all progress will be lost. This program was totally exhausting for our family. Luckily, my dear mother-in-law, Lucia, told me of the *Son-rise* Program. And after watching their videos online, I decided to try their philosophy and see what happened. I was really excited! What if this worked?! What if the scream he'd ritualistically let out as I walked toward him to stop this behavior, ceased to escape his mouth? So, I approached him. That look of sadness and concern, which I usually wore on my face during this routine, was replaced with a smile of anticipation and excitement of a new game. My steps were light and slower paced on purpose, as to let them tell Matteo that these were new steps of acceptance, not the old ones of judgment. I arrived and stood about three feet down the fence from him. He looked my direction and started to let the scream out, but stopped after just a peep. I did not look at him because I was excited to gather my own twigs and tiny rocks. I began my own game of gently throwing them over the fence into our neighbor's driveway. I got really into it, just as I had learned on the videos. I seriously don't remember how long I'd been involved in my game, but I do remember the moment I stopped and looked at Matteo, who had a look of amazement on his face. Seriously, his mouth was hanging wide open and his eyes looked as if he'd seen a ghost or even better, a chocolate bar as big as a semi truck! He was watching me in total amazement, as if to say, "Who are you and who took my mom?"

Then it happened...I smiled at him to silently say, "Thanks for noticing me, Buddy." And the most beautiful smile stretched across his face. My heart leapt and tears of joy followed. I wanted to run to him and grab my beautiful eight-year-old boy in my arms with the biggest embrace in the world, but I refrained, out of respect and a deep desire to prolong the most life-altering moment in our relationship.

Well, that was it, off to *Son-Rise* training we went. Mark and I both came back from that week in Massachusetts with new spirits, a renewed marriage, and greater love and respect for our son than we ever thought possible. We always loved him, but I wouldn't say that "respect" was an adjective I would choose to describe my attitude toward him back then. Sure, I respected him as a person, but not for the amazingly unique way he functions in this world and the challenges he overcomes to exist each day in a place so overloaded with sensory information and negative judgments of those who are different than society's "norm." To acquire that type of respect, I had to peel back many, many layers of myself and be willing to "go there" with deep, personal and emotional questions,

questions capable of stirring such emotion in me that I had chosen to bury or deny them. I guess I thought that was a much wiser (and certainly easier) choice at the time.

Our current respect for our son is off the charts, as he can now explain exactly why he does certain things and how this world affects him. To know what it feels like in his body and mind is the biggest gift we could ever have been blessed to receive. His ability to share his insights into his own neurology and physical body has helped us tailor his therapies. Now, the sky's the limit!

I get asked by parents all the time, "How can I bond with my autistic child? It seems like he isn't interested in me, at all. I'm just a tool to him." I know that the way autistics use their bodies could paint that picture. I'll tell you that when I learned to look at my son with curiosity instead of an underlying frustration and judgment, life changed for us. I realized I was actually judging his inability to conform to society's expectations while disregarding how difficult life is for him and how uncooperative his body is on this Earth. I began my detective work. I'd get down to his height and follow his gaze to see what was more exciting than I was. It was actually really fun! The feeling inside me and the energy behind how I acted changed.

Matteo has shared that he feels these energy shifts in me immediately and that they are magnified inside of him. Valuable information!

You've heard the idea, "your children are mirror images of you?" Well, it is so true in my life. I have noticed that when I have a challenging day or have dealt with crazy rush hour traffic and my energy is, shall we say, "challenged," Matteo has a very difficult and frustrating time interacting with me. It's like he says, "Talk to the hand, Mom. Come back when you find some patience." That word keeps popping back into my head...perspective.

As Teo has been writing this book, I found myself reliving many experiences of his early childhood. So much of the emotion of those earlier years would actually be tough to relive if I let it be, as I am not that person anymore. The contrast between now and then, in my attitude and the way I see my son, myself and my husband, is drastic. It's night and day.

Just as I thought I'd learned and recognized my lessons from those earlier years, new "a-ha" moments would bust through as I took dictation from his letter board. One, then another, then another! Did you see the first Harry Potter movie? Remember when Harry got his first letter from Hogwarts but his mean uncle wouldn't let him see it? So the Wizards sent more and more letters, through the mail slot, down the chimney, through the windows, under the door, through cracks in the walls, filling up the house with these letters. Eventually, Harry would get hold of one and the message would be delivered. That's how I've felt scribing for Teo during the creation of this book. Message after message being hand-delivered to me.

We began the first chapters back in August of 2015, only four months after Teo began *RPM* with Lenae. I had read the books and was doing the basics of "teach-ask" with him for 4 months prior to getting to meet with Lenae, so Teo was ready to start sharing his thoughts pretty quickly. Plus, I just *knew* this was the answer and miracle we'd been waiting for, which would enable him to communicate his deep thoughts and opinions. I didn't approach this method thinking, "I hope this works" or "This has to work!" or "I'll give it a try." Behind this attitude was and still is, a confidence that is unwavering, no matter what each individual day brings. I just choose it, each and every day. Some days are more challenging than others for us to communicate, but then we talk about it openly. What do we want to do about it? Get frustrated and continue anyway, having a complicated, forced, stressful interaction? Basically, prolonged torture? Or should we just take it as a sign that it's time to go outside and enjoy the sun, get some exercise or go on a field trip instead?

Oh, the beauty of home-schooling! I won't even tell you our answer. It's quite obvious and I love that we have created a learning environment for our son that allows such freedom! It's freedom that is based on his needs and wants and takes into account his individual uniqueness as a human being. Talk about a real Individualized Education Plan! Here is ours:

Goal 1: Happiness and Joy

Matteo will live a joyous life. Success will be based on his energy and open discussions of his feelings using *RPM*. Strategies will be implemented by people in his life with open minds and hearts.

Goal 2: Eye Contact

Matteo will make eye contact and hold a gaze with anyone he chooses. Those receiving the eye contact will smile and their hearts will rejoice.

Goal 3: Academics

Matteo will participate in academic learning of Core Curriculum studies at his own pace. Increasing tolerance will always be a continuous, gradual goal.

Goal 4: Education

Academic requirements will be interspersed with amazing, challenging topics which are of interest to him or just blatantly cool things to know. The teaching team will introduce him to a wide range of topics and Matteo will then tell them which of those he'd like to study more in depth. These topics may include, but are not limited to cooking, music, camping, swimming, cycling, hiking, marine biology, religions of the world, politics, world history, the use of math and physics in everyday life, current events and public service opportunities, etc.

Goal 5: Social Skills

Matteo will engage with peers, both autistic and neuro-typical, anytime he chooses. Social opportunities will take place when they present themselves and academics will be done at a time when his learning channels are most easily accessible and ready. That's usually not when he hears the neighbor kids playing outside and riding their bikes in the court. Go play, my friend...be a kid!

We've got it pretty easy in that Matteo wants to learn about everything! His thirst for knowledge is remarkable. He's expressed that because he has been deprived of a formal education and exposure to interesting things for his entire life. So, we don't have the struggles that some parents might have to educate our son. When asked if he'd rather have a "lesson" or watch a movie, most often, he'll choose to have a lesson. It's me who wants to plop on the couch, have a glass of chardonnay and watch the movie!

I am far from being a perfect mother. I am far from being made entirely of patience. I am far from having solved every challenge facing my son for the rest of his life. I am far from having it all figured out. But I now recognize that I live with the most creative teacher in the world, my own personal *Buddha* of sorts. Although I am far from perfect, I am grateful that I recognize these teaching moments from him as learning opportunities for me. I seize them as often as I am humanly able at this time. Believe me, my tolerance and willingness as a student may differ every day, but I continue to try. When I fail or get frustrated, I apologize and speak openly and honestly with Teo about it. Respect.

Then he tells me, over and over, "It's OK, Mom. That's all I want. You're evolving nicely and I love you."

Enjoy your own evolution,
Annette

Keep in touch!

•

Website:
www.matteomusso.com

Blog:
www.pedalingwithteo.com

Facebook:
Annette Musso, Livermore, CA
https://www.facebook.com/annette.musso

Email:
info@matteomusso.com

I really look forward to hearing from you!

Recommended Resources

www.halo-soma.org
HALO=Helping Autism through Learning and Outreach

This is the website about *SOMA RPM* and it is full of resources! There are "frequently asked questions," videos of Soma herself, teaching students with various neurological challenges and a "resource" section where you may purchase books and letter boards.

www.heedrpm.com
Hope, Expression and Education

Lenae Crandall is the *RPM* specialist/teacher with whom we study and our ANGEL. Through her love and dedication, our lives are changed forever. This is her website. It is a great "teaching" website full of information gathered from Lenae's experiences working with hundreds of students all around the world.

www.acetc.info

This is the website and organization of another really well-respected *SOMA RPM* teacher. She has started a school in Wisconsin where *RPM* is teaching the methodology.

www.masgutovamethod.com

Dr. Svetlana Masgutova, creator of the *MNRI – Neurosensorimotor Reflex Integration Program*. This primitive reflex work feels like massage on my body. It has helped me tremendously in a wide variety of ways and I love it so much!

www.ehealing.org

Master Behrooz Donadoost, *Shafaw Sanctuary of Healing Light*. Shafaw literally means "miraculous healing." This energy work has helped me in so many ways, especially to feel grounded. I am grateful that Mom and Dad were open to it.

www.castcal.org

This is my mom's non-profit organization, *Creative Autism Solutions Team*. This is where you can donate to further my mission and that of so many of my esteemed colleagues on the autism spectrum.

www.autismtreatmentcenter.org

This is the *Son-Rise* program's website. It can really help you find inner peace on your journey with us.

My website:

www.matteomusso.com

My Blog:

www.pedalingwithteo.com

This is a blog that I wanted to start. We post new information/videos as they come up and as we think appropriate for public viewing and interest.

"*What If*" series of children's books:
These books were written by my mom to teach children to embrace and celebrate our differences.

What if we all looked the same?

What if we all only liked chocolate?

What if we all learned the same?

Get ready for: *The Treatons Are Coming!*

Available at amazon.com *or* matteomusso.com

Made in the USA
Monee, IL
31 May 2021